THIRTEEN MONTHS

THIRTEEN
MONTHS

K.W. Gorsky, Jr.

To Rich & Michele

K.W. Gorsky

VANTAGE PRESS
New York / Los Angeles / Chicago

Published by Vantage Press, Inc.
516 West 34th Street, New York, New York 10001

Manufactured in the United States of America
ISBN: 0-533-08014-2

Library of Congress Catalog Card No.: 88-90133

To all who served . . .
and understood

Contents

Preface

The Vietnam War evolved into a politically controversial under-taking of the United States government. In retrospect, it exposed the lives of many thousands of young Americans to a deadly calcu-lated, no win conflict. Not only did the war violently split the American populace, but it also irreversibly scarred the men and women who, on the whole, diligently served in the armed forces of the United States, just as our forefathers did when they were called to arms.

For the most part, young men and women went to Vietnam with the notion that they were serving their country and were de-fending democracy; however, what they actually experienced there and what they had to endure there eroded their ideals some-what. Consequently, everyone did not necessarily return home be-lieving in their ideals as strongly as they did before they served in Vietnam.

The Vietnam War produced its share of tragedies and at-rocities, but at the same time it also engendered heroes; and there were many. Those that gave the ultimate to their country should al-ways be remembered, and those that returned physically impaired or mentally scarred should never be forsaken.

Now that more than a decade has passed, there is an underly-ing desire, I believe, for the Vietnam veteran to yield his experi-ences no matter how gruesome or insignificant those experiences may seem.

This novel depicts the real life experiences of one marine who, at the tender age of eighteen, served his country halfway around the world in that unpopular war.

THIRTEEN
MONTHS

1.   Arrival

It was late morning (3 March 1968) when our commercial airliner
began its descent and prepared to land in Da Nang. I immediately
felt a downward pressure as the plane's powerful engines were
throttled back. Their high-pitched whine mellowed to a lower, less
annoying drone. A brief glance through the window revealed that
we were still flying over water, although I could clearly see the
coastline in the distance. I was truly impressed with the serene
beauty of the bluish green waters beneath us. As my thoughts became transfixed, they were suddenly interrupted by the captain's
dulcet voice: "Welcome to sunny Vietnam. The ground temperature is one hundred and one degrees. We've been advised that the
last plane to land here took some mortars. . . . Please fasten your
seat—"

The sudden sound of my heart fiercely pounding in my ears
blocked out his voice. I knew that it would only be a few minutes
before the plane touched down on the runway, and for the first time
I realized that I was really scared about going to Vietnam.

Since we had left Okinawa, the atmosphere in the plane had
changed abruptly from joking around and flirting with the stewardesses to an almost silent and pensive mood. I was assigned to the
seat nearest the window and sat next to a sailor named Bill Press for
the flight over. As the hours passed, we found that we had little in
common, other than being eighteen years old and both being on

our way to war. Nevertheless, we acted like old buddies and talked about our hometowns, girl friends, and high schools. We also shared both my anxieties and his fears. He was a southerner who had joined the navy to see the world and was now assigned to a ship off the coast of Vietnam as a mail clerk. He was scared to death. I could see the fear in his face, and he had no qualms about expressing it. As for me, I enlisted in the Marine Corps a month after graduating from high school and was anxious to serve my country in Vietnam. It's what I had often thought about as I was growing up.

As far back as I could remember, the military had always greatly intrigued me. I possessed the secret desire to attend military school but knew that my folks did not have the financial resources to enroll me. Consequently, the desire was never fulfilled. Even as a young boy, my childhood friends and I oftentimes pretended to play army. We donned uniforms, toted toy guns, staged mock military battles, and fought fiercely through dangerous backyards, over treacherous fences, and atop precarious garage roofs. Moreover, on Sunday mornings I religiously tuned in to "The Big Picture," a World War II saga narrated by Walter Cronkite. Even then, I found myself fantasizing about fighting in a war. Invariably, patriotism and duty to my country had been fundamentally ingrained in my character from an early age. It was now my turn—I was going to war.

All kinds of thoughts raced through my mind in a split second: Would the plane get hit with a mortar? Would I get wounded as soon as we arrived? How far do we have to run for cover? No one on the plane had weapons or combat gear. We had boarded the plane with only our seabags and hand carried out ditty bags.

Before I realized it, the plane had landed and taxied to the debarkation area. Once again, the captain's voice came over the PA system wishing us all a safe tour. The stewardesses directed us toward the exit with a pleasant smile and wished each of us luck as we passed. As I reached the door, a rush of hot and pungent air struck me like a slap in the face. It was a totally unexpected change from the air-conditioned plane. Instantly, the overwhelmingly pungent odor became permanently etched in my mind. I would never forget it.

As we departed the plane and urgently double-timed across the flight line toward a distant building some four hundred meters away, I could feel the noonday sun penetrating my heavy stateside utilities, which quickly became uncomfortable after running over what seemed to be boiling tarmac. Sweat began streaming down the sides of my face and into my eyes. Whatever material my uniform was made out of, it certainly wasn't made for Vietnam. That was for sure. Everyone sought relief in the shade of the white building but found it offered little.

Like everyone else, I hand-carried my new orders with me, along with my service, medical, and pay records. I had been assigned to the First Marine Division, and my best buddy, John Todd, had been issued orders for the Third Marine Division. We both arrived on the same plane and met up in the receiving area inside the shady, but not any cooler, building.

John and I first met in staging, at Camp Pendleton, California. We were in the same platoon and bunked together on the second floor. He was a short, dark-haired, and somewhat quiet guy from New York and I was from New Jersey. Since we were virtually neighbors back home, we hit it off well right from the start. We were both there for training before going to Vietnam. The training was tough and crammed into a short three and a half weeks. Camp Pendleton was chock-full of mountains, and we must have humped all of them several times over. One day, halfway through the training, we were practicing disarming land mines when ours blew up. As punishment for being so careless, John and I had to double-time to the top of Sheep Shit Mountain and back down again. We found out the hard way how it got its name!

and I were no exceptions. We spent all of ours together and our friendship grew rapidly. John frequently needed prodding to write letters back home to his girl friend. He just wasn't a letter writer, and she wrote to him often. Unlike John, I was always writing home to someone.

On our last weekend liberty before shipping out for Vietnam, John and I rented a car just outside the base, along with two other guys from our platoon. Jim Reelings had to sign the rental contract because he was the only one who was old enough, at age twenty-one. The four of us had already been south of the border to Tijuana, so we decided to try our luck in Anaheim. We hadn't traveled far when the car broke down and we had to push it to a gas station a short distance away, all uphill. Our luck seemed to improve a little when the station owner turned out to be an ex-Marine Corps gunnery sergeant. He fixed the car at no charge, and in no time flat we were on our way again.

Our weekend liberty was over before we knew it, and somehow we missed the bus that would get us back to the barracks before morning muster; so we grabbed a quick breakfast in town, mulled over what might happen to us for being late, and then caught the next bus in. Finally, we came strolling in, still dressed in civies, as Sergeant Phillips was dismissing the formation. He was rightly pissed off and ordered us to report to the OD's office after changing into uniform. We took our time and figured the worst that could happen was that they would send us to Nam, and we were going anyway, so it really didn't matter much.

Later that day, word came down from the company commander that we would all be moving out the next morning, so we all got our gear squared away and made last minute phone calls. I slipped away and went to the PX. While I was gone, Sergeant Phillips put John on a work detail swabbing the squadbay, so I made sure I stayed clear of Sergeant Phillips for the rest of the day.

There was no off-base liberty for anyone that night. They wanted to make sure that we would all be there in the morning. Surprisingly, I had no trouble sleeping that night and found myself chomping at the bit when reveille sounded.

After morning chow, at first formation, the CO and Sergeant Phillips made a short gung ho speech before we boarded the buses. Sergeant Phillips and the CO had completed a tour in Nam and knew what was in store for us; they knew some of us would not be coming back home.

John and I chewed the fat the entire ride to the airport. We both agreed, once we knew what our mailing addresses were, that we would write to one another's folks and give them the addresses so that we could keep in touch while we were in Nam. John promised me he would write.

Inside the white receiving building at Da Nang's air base, marines were milling around everywhere. Some were stretched out on the few benches that could be found. Others, who were less fortunate, were sitting on the floor with their backs propped up against one of the steel columns. Still others were standing around drinking Coca-Cola in small bottles and talking about body counts. Most were wearing faded jungle utilities, combat gear, mud-caked jungle boots, and carrying M-16s. They looked like they had just walked out of the jungle. In sharp contrast, we were sporting our starched stateside utilities, spit-shined combat boots, and were ordinarily pale compared to their sunbaked complexions. One could easily tell who was new in the country.

While waiting to be told what to do next, I was eyeballing the area. The building we were standing in was only one story, L-shaped, open on two sides, and had a cement floor with steel I beam columns supporting a flat roof. There was a window on one wall with a red stenciled sign above it that read DISBURSING. On the other wall was a red painted door. On it, stenciled in yellow, were the words MACV OFFICE I CORPS.

Suddenly, a marine corporal appeared and announced to all new arrivals that we had to report to the disbursing window and exchange any U.S. currency we had for military payments certificates (MPC). It was difficult to hear him over the almost constant din of combat jet fighters and choppers taking off and landing nearby. John and I got on line and waited our turn to exchange our money. I didn't have much and John had even less. We were surprised to learn that MPC was all paper money, including change. It took awhile getting accustomed to. (I later found MPC useful as earplugs during fire missions.) I asked the corporal behind the window, "What are we supposed to do now?"

He appeared slightly annoyed and curtly asked, "What do your orders say?"

I hesitated for a second and then explained, "I'm going to the First Division, and my buddy here is going to the Third."

He sharply instructed, "Just relax and don't wander away from the area. Someone will be here soon to pick you up. They'll transport you to wherever you're supposed to report in."

I didn't know about John, but I felt a little confused not knowing what was going to happen next. I began to realize how much difference there was between being in Nam and being back in the World. In Nam, most of the rules seemed to have gone out of the window. I told myself, "The sooner I learn the rules they play by here, the better off I'll be."

We walked around the outside of the building and in the back came across a Vietnamese girl selling ice-cold Coca-Cola for 25 cents, MPC. In amazement, I looked at John and said, "How do you like that shit? Here we are halfway around the world and some kid is selling us Coca-Cola."

We each bought one with our new MPC and hastily chugalugged them down. I needed something to replenish my body fluids in the oppressive heat.

It didn't seem long when a first lieutenant showed up with a roster of new replacements for the Third Marine Division. The time for us to part had come. John's name was on the list. We shook hands and said our good-byes. The last thing I said was, "Don't forget to write!"

I watched him carry his seabag out to the flight line. Before he climbed on board the chopper, he turned and threw a salute in my direction. I didn't know it then, but that was the last time I would ever see John.

A feeling of loneliness began to creep into my thoughts. Most of the guys I knew had just left for the Third Division. I looked around and could count only five guys that I recognized. They had been part of my company during training, back at Camp Pendleton, but were from different platoons. No one was left now from my own.

I glanced down at my watch; it was 1417 hours. We had landed at approximately 1130 hours. I had adjusted my watch earlier on the plane when the stewardess had announced the correct time in Vietnam.

I was feeling hungry but was afraid to go searching for a chow hall because I might miss my transportation, although I didn't know when it was coming. Anyway, the corporal told us not to wander out of the area. I spotted an empty bench vacated by some of the guys who had left for the Third Division. I had dumped my seabag near that same bench when we first arrived, so I sat down, placed my feet on it, and took the corporal's advice; I relaxed.

Sometime later, a six-by truck pulled up next to the building and made an inherently noisy stop. The driver remained in the cab while a second lieutenant climbed out from the shotgun side. He looked the part of an officer. My guess was that only someone from the higher echelon would be wearing a starched utility hat with his rank insignia pinned to it, new jungle utilities, bloused trousers, shined jungle boots, and a .45 automatic in a polished holster tied to his leg. He resembled a recruiting poster. Standing in the open back of the truck was another marine, wearing a helmet and flak jacket over a faded green T-shirt. He seemed to be manning an M-60 machine gun mounted to the roof of the cab.

The lieutenant looked around, quickly brushed off his jungles, stretched his shoulders, and pulled at his crotch; then he strutted into the building. I thought for a second that I recognized him from somewhere; however, when he got a little closer, I realized that I was mistaken. He pulled a roster from his pocket, unfolded it, and declared in a somewhat southern drawl, "Anyone with orders for the First Marine Division, get your gear on the truck and sound off with your name."

I immediately realized that we couldn't be going too great of a distance, since we weren't going by chopper. I grabbed my gear, went to the rear of the truck, and threw it on board. When I turned around, the lieutenant was standing right there holding the paper in one hand, while he casually rested the other on his holster. His presence startled me for an instant. When I recovered, I quickly blurted out my name and rank. He slowly scrutinized the roster, found it halfway down the list, and checked it off. With pencil in hand, he motioned toward the truck and barked, "Okay, PFC, get on. We'll be pulling out in a minute or two."

Several others got on after me and found seats in the back of the truck. The truck had two wooden benches where one could sit on either side. All of our gear was piled in the middle and we sat facing one another. Just before we started out, the lieutenant informed us that we were headed for regimental headquarters. Someone asked him which one and he replied, "The Seventh. So make yourselves comfortable; it's about a twenty minute haul."

The driver started the engine of the two-and-half-ton truck and it lurched forward. He made a sharp left turn and we bounced several times until the truck was finally onto the paved road. Sitting in the back seemed to have the advantage of getting a breeze as we drove along. The driver followed a road that lead us through what I later discovered to be the First Marine Division's headquarters area. The buildings were all neatly squared away with white painted rocks lining the road and trees that shaded the area everywhere one looked. Each of the buildings we passed had a cement walk leading up to the entrance and was bordered by a white chain strung between several two-foot-high metal posts.

We made two stops along the way when the lieutenant got out

and instructed us to stay put. The marine manning the M-60 explained to us that we were on the daily admin run and that was the reason for all the stops. I reasoned to myself that the lieutenant was either delivering or collecting dispatches of some sort. He had only been a few minutes at each stop. Then we were going again.

Soon, we made our way through what appeared to be a rear gate. The driver turned onto a well-traveled dirt road that had only one lane in each direction. In contrast to its starkly barren surroundings, the road was crammed with military vehicles, bicycles, motorcycles, overcrowded minibuses, and Vietnamese walking along the sides. The driver had no choice but to slowly ease along in traffic. The first intersection we approached had a tank posted at the corner on top of a huge dirt mound overlooking the intersection. Next to it stood a dilapidated road sign marked ROUTE ONE.

As the truck continued, the traffic began to lessen. We passed through several villes where the people were all going about their daily chores totally oblivious to the traffic only a few feet away from their hooches. Old men with conical straw hats were squatting in the shade, little children with even smaller babies in their arms were waving at just about any military vehicle that passed by, and old women with blackened teeth, dressed in silk pajamas, swept the ground around them. Occasionally, when traffic slowed to a stop, some little baby-san would come running up to the truck clenching two bottles in each hand and chirping, "Hey, numbah one GI . . . you buy Coke?"

I felt like I was sightseeing—a tourist just riding through. It wasn't what I had anticipated. *Shockingly primitive!* was what immediately came to mind. It seemed like all my senses were being bombarded at once by the immediate surroundings: the pungent odor permeating the air; the stifling arid heat; the throat-parching dust; the exotic language of the Vietnamese people; and their wretchedly crude living conditions. I really didn't know what to make of it all and found the profusion much too perplexing for any serious thought.

My attention was soon drawn toward a rather large hill in the near distance. Our six-by steadily approached along a winding dirt road flanked on both sides by evenly sectioned rice paddies. As I looked behind us, all I could see was a huge dust cloud created by the speed of the truck over the dried out road. Ahead of us the road forked in two directions and the driver bore hard to the right. We traveled a short distance before the rice paddies abruptly ended. Our speed slowly decreased and we began to traverse an ever-increasing incline as the six-by labored onward.

When we reached the top, the truck came to a rolling stop and the driver waved to the two guards posted at the sandbagged bunker positioned there. Then we crept along a road that wound its way through rows of paintless wooden structures with metal roofs and big tents on wooden platforms. We passed a rather large chow hall and continued down a small ridge. Finally, the truck pulled into an area that appeared to be an amphitheater. There in the center was a green platform, about two feet high and twenty feet square, with several stairs leading up the front, and surrounded by open area all the way around. This was the end of the ride. We had arrived at the Seventh Marine Regiment.

We removed our gear from the truck and piled it on the wooden platform as we were instructed. Before the six-by drove away, the lieutenant told ut to get some chow if we wanted to and be back at 1800 hours.

I discovered that there were more disadvantages to riding in the back of the truck then I had thought. I was completely covered form head to toe with road dust, my ass hurt from the wooden bench, and my vision finally adjusted after seeing everything bounce by as we drove along. I had been sitting next to the tailgate for most of the trip. That's the first thing I learned not to do again. In Nam, everyone quickly became accustomed to bone-rattling transportation.

After I downed a good meal at the chow hall, I decided to

have a look around the area. As I wandered around, it suddenly dawned on me that a friend of mine named Juan, who I knew from back home, was with Mike Company, First Battalion, Seventh Marines, and that he was in a country a good few months already. Just ahead of me, several guys were sitting around on wooden ammo boxes shooting the breeze. I stopped to inquire if they knew where Mike Company, First Battalion was. One black sergeant obligingly answered, "Sure thing, Slick! Two hooches down on the right."

As I walked down there I felt an excitement building up inside me, just to think that we would be on the same hill in Nam, so far away from home. It would be great to see him again, I thought.

I turned between two hooches and made my way around to the rear. There I found four marines eating C-rats and drinking beer. They seemed to be enjoying themselves. Suddenly, I felt as though I was intruding. Nevertheless, I said to the one sitting on top of a fifty-five gallon drum, "Excuse me! I'm looking for Juan Celone. Do you know him?"

Another marine who was sitting on the ground reading a letter looked up and said, "Yeah, but he's not here anymore. He got hit in the leg with some shrapnel at Liberty Bridge a couple of days ago."

"How bad was it?" I cringed.

"Not too bad. He'll make it." There was a short silence and he asked, "How do you know him?"

"We were friends back home. . . . He lived up the block from me."

"Yeah, well, he was our squad leader when we got ambushed at that fuckin' bridge."

"Everybody in the squad liked him," added the marine on the drum. Then there was another long and awkward silence.

"Well . . . thanks," I said, still feeling out of place. "I've gotta be getting back. If you do see him again, tell him Ski was here looking for him. He'll know who was here."

. I left feeling very disappointed that Juan wasn't there and that

I didn't get to see him after all. I wondered if he really would be okay or not. I saw that it was getting close to the time we were supposed to be back, and the sun had just about set, so I backtracked to the amphitheater and waited with the others.

Dusk began to creep over the hill, and the heat of the day steadily subsided. By then, everyone had returned and most were milling around the platform. Soon a Hispanic-looking captain, sporting a handlebar mustache and wearing starched utilities, mounted the platform. He announced that we would be spending the night and would be leaving first thing in the morning, after the road sweep. He continued by telling us we would have to sleep on the platform and to be ready to leave by 0945 hours. "—the battalion admin run will take you back with them, so be here when they're ready to leave," he finished saying.

By that time I was getting tired and welcomed the opportunity to get some sleep. It wasn't dark yet, so I picked a spot near the edge of the platform, in case I needed to get off fast, arranged my gear and made myself comfortable. As the twilight faded into darkness, the stars began to appear one at a time. Soon there seemed to be millions of them scattered from horizon to horizon. I gazed at the stars and wondered where we would be headed the next day as I nodded off to sleep.

Several times during the night I woke to the sound of artillery firing. At first it startled me, but after nervously looking around I concluded that the firing was outgoing and I relaxed slightly. Just as I began to fall back to sleep for the last time, a flare popped and bathed the area in an eerie light. I watched it as it began to drift toward us, slowly floating downward, and then die out. I didn't know why it was popped. Maybe somebody thought they saw something, or heard something. Who knows? Nothing more happened after that. Everything was quiet again.

Morning slowly brought activity back to the hill, and the chow hall attracted everyone like a magnet. I was no exception. I thought it best to get there early before a line formed. I stretched the kinks out of my neck and strolled up the hill to chow. As it turned out, I had arrived just in time, a few minutes later and I would have been standing in a long line. Once inside, the smell of french toast and sausage permeated the air; however, I chose scrambled eggs and bacon. I found an empty table, sat down, and ate. It was 0645 hours and I was ready to go. I gulped down my second cup of black coffee and made room for someone else to eat.

The admin run was twenty minutes late arriving on the hill. Later, I learned the driver couldn't use the road until the morning road sweep was completed. I surmised that they must have had some sort of trouble along the way. When the six-by arrived there were three others on board already: two marines in the back and a sergeant riding shotgun. The driver stuck his head out the window and shouted toward us, "I was told to pick you guys up and take you back with us. Load your gear on and let's go."

The truck had a water bull hitched to the back. It looked like it could hold about five hundred gallons of water, and it sat on two wheels. This time I made sure that I sat near the cab of the truck and not near the tailgate. After everyone was on board, the driver negotiated around the platform and back up the incline. We made our way through the area to the main gate and left the same way we had arrived the day before.

We drove for some time, occasionally passing a ville or another truck on the road. It seemed desolate except for the open rice paddies and the mountains in the distance. The truck raced along the road like someone was chasing us. Suddenly a fear started to build up inside me. We were riding along in the middle of Vietnam and I didn't have a weapon if something happened. Neither did anyone else, except for the two marines with M-16s. I thought this was pretty stupid and I began praying that nothing would happen.

As we turned off the main road, the driver took the turn so fast that he almost lost the water bull. It rounded the turn teetering on only one wheel and then righted itself again. One of the marines with the M-16s must have read the look of fear on my face and explained to me that the driver had taken the long way to Third Battalion. The shorter route was by way of Liberty Bridge, but that had been blow up by the gooks a few days before. Then he indicated that we had arrived and that I didn't need to worry anymore.

We proceeded along a spiral road, which lead to the top of the hill. Although it wasn't as steep as the regiment's hill, it was still a hefty incline nonetheless. I noticed that the color of the road dirt changed to a dark brown, almost like it was wet. As though it was on cue, someone jokingly remarked, "It smells like diesel fuel around here."

The same marine who had consoled me before said, "Yeah, they spray diesel fuel on the road to keep the dust down."

We drove onto the hill along a dirt road lined with concertina wire, continued past a staging area for tanks and amtracks, and skirted the ammo dump. Sluggishly, we made our way to the far side of the hill, where the truck finally stopped at the admin hooch marked HEADQUARTERS 3/7.

There, we reported in and spent a considerable amount of time getting our paperwork processed. After we were finished, a sergeant showed me and two others to a hooch that was at the end of a long row of similar looking ones. It was a large tent draped over screened-in sides, with a bare wooden floor and wooden screen doors at each end. One end of the hooch was at ground level and the other had three steps leading up to it.

When we entered, there were only a few guys inside. The sergeant told us to find empty bunks for ourselves. There was a small area near the front door that was about eight feet long and fifteen feet wide and was partitioned off from the rest of the hooch. In it were four cots, two on each side—one was empty. That one became mine. On the other side of the partition were twelve more cots and an aisle that ran from door to door through the center of the hooch. Several bare light bulbs were strung from one end to the other and dangled above the aisle.

This was the hooch for 81s, H&S Company. My MOS was 0341 (infantry: mortar man).

2.

A-gunner

Out of nowhere, a baritone voice sharply bellowed, "I don't believe this!"

I glanced up from what I was doing to discover a black guy standing at the foot of my bunk. His surprise-riddled face was accentuated by the protruding whites of his eyes. At that same instant, I recognized Lou Atkins, who I had trained with in boot camp at Parris Island. I never expected to run into anyone in Nam that I knew, but there he was. He and several other marines had just walked into the hooch.

"Lou?" I blurted out in disbelief. "I can't believe my eyes!" Impulsively, I jumped to my feet and greeted him with a hardy handshake.

He embraced me in an expression of comradeship and cried, "It's great to see ya again, Ski!"

"You, too!" I said. Then there was a short pause as the initial shock wore off.

"So when did you get in?" he asked, still embracing my shoulder.

"Oh, about an hour ago," I said, glancing at my watch. "I came in on the admin run and just finished checking in at the battalion admin hooch; then some sergeant brought me and a couple of other guys down here and told us to grab a bunk, so I took this one. Is it okay?"

"Yeah, that's fine. I bunk right over here!" he said, pointing to his rack. It was mere coincidence that I had chosen the bunk right next to his. The other two bunks, I found out later, belonged to the two squad leaders. "Come on, Ski, let me show you around," he said as he lead me into the back section of the hooch. He introduced me to everyone present, telling them that we had gone through both boot camp and ITR together back in the World.

Our chance reunion was just what the doctor had ordered. Lou seemed as delighted to see me as I was to see him. I was very thankful that he was there, for his presence eased my anxieties a great deal. The difficult part was dealing with the sobering realities of Nam itself, and that I could only do alone.

Lou and I spent the rest of the afternoon reminiscing about old times and reflecting upon who from our original platoon had already become casualties. When it came time to show me around the area, Lou took me on the grand tour, pointing out where everything important was located on the hill: the chow hall, the latrines, the water bull, et cetera. He even went along when I had to report to battalion supply to draw my gear and my weapon. The last thing Lou did was warn me about drinking too much of the chlorinated water, at least until I was used to it. It could make one awfully sick.

I was issued two sets of jungles, a helmet, flak jacket, rifle belt, two canteens, E-tool, poncho and liner, gas mask, and pack. Unfortunately for me, they were out of my size jungle boots and the supply sergeant had no idea when they would receive a new supply of them. In the meantime, I had to make due with my only pair of all leather combat boots. At the armory, I was issued an M-16, four magazines, some cleaning gear, and several bandoliers of ammo. I was happy with the thought of finally being issued a weapon.

Eighty-ones were an integral component of each and every grunt company. They were highly touted as crew-served, close-fire support weapons. A two–gun squad mortar section, consisting of eighteen men, was attached to each company. Whenever the company operated out of the gun's range (four clicks or about two miles), they had to go along; otherwise, only the forward observer (FO) and the radioman (RO) went along, thus directing the high-angle support fire from the base camp.

A gun squad was made up of a squad leader, gunner, A-gunner, and four ammo humpers. Each man was responsible for a certain job and his specific part of the gun. The gun squad that Harvey Neils and I were assigned to was well below the prescribed TO. We immediately filled the slots of the second and third ammo humpers in the squad when we arrived. Still and all, the squad was one man short and the burden fell directly upon us to take up the slack.

My job was breaking out ammo and, if necessary, humping around the inner ring of the base plate.

Harvey's responsibility was taking care of the aiming stakes and assisting me with the ammo. Harvey, with his thin face and infectious smile, always delighted in the look of disbelief on people's faces when he was asked where he was from back in the World. With a serious scowl on his face he would blurt out, "Intercourse, PA." Then, immediately, the scowl would change to a sardonic grin, as that person recovered from the shock of his answer.

Lou was the first ammo humper, responsible for the outer ring of the base plate and for handing the rounds to the A-gunner. Lou was a dark-skinned black from New York who had close-cropped hair resembling brillow; at least I teased him about it looking that way. As far as his facial features were concerned, he reminded me a little of Louie Armstrong, but lacking his musical ability.

The A-gunner was Sam Banks, a rowdy southern rebel boy. It was his job to drop the rounds down the tube. He was a short-timer and was ready to rotate back to the World.

The gunner was Vic Tasuello. His sole responsibility was setting up the gun. He was a tall, olive complexioned Italian with a somewhat impetuous disposition, who hailed from Linden, New Jersey.

The squad leader, Fred Barefield, was short also. He was due to rotate in a few weeks. As his name implied, he was a big brawny individual with a thick black mustache. His nickname was Bear. He had an annoying habit of continuously stroking the corners of his mustache whenever he talked to anyone and became infuriated when it was brought to his attention.

Finally, there was the section leader, Sergeant Stacker, the assistant section leader, Corporal Lewis, the RO, and last but not least, the FO. I never met the RO nor the FO. All of them lived and worked out of our Fire Directional Center (FDC) located between the gun pits, thereby affording me little opportunity to get to know them.

The first few nights after I had arrived at battalion, I found myself detailed on hole watch. One of our gun squads pulled perimeter watch each night while the other had gun duty. Just before dark, we would take up positions in the bunkers and trenches that lined the entire perimeter of the hill. Two men were most often assigned to each bunker—sometimes three. Usually, both men would stay awake for the first several hours and then take turns on watch while the other grabbed some sleep. The bunker positions would then be secured at daybreak.

On the second night in particular, Harvey and I pulled watch in one of the point bunkers located on the northern end of the hill. We shot the bull through the early part of the evening, before Harvey took the first watch. I decided that instead of going to sleep, I would use the time to write a letter. I crouched next to Harvey, covered myself with my poncho, so the light of my flashlight wouldn't be seen, and scribed a few lines in the dim light. Shortly after, I fell asleep.

Around 0200 hours, the back side of the hill sounded like it took several rockets. Within seconds, the word was passed along that we were taking incoming. Both Harvey and I expected contact at our end of the hill at any second, largely due to where our position was situated. Our bunker sat precariously upon a little embankment directly above the main access road. From there we had a clear view over a wide span of nearly flat land. To the far right, but still in our line of fire, was a large mound of loose dirt. Directly in front of us, and strung with a triple row of concertina wire, was the access road. It was terribly quiet and extremely dark out there. Not even the moon's reflected light rendered us the slightest assistance.

The adrenalin raced through my blood, and I felt both scared and excited at the same time. With the passing of each minute, Harvey and I became unnerved with anticipation. Recently, there had been a considerable amount of North Vietnamese army (NVA) activity in our immediate area, due to their massive push during Tet—only a month ago, but the remainder of the night passed without further incident, proving our fears to be unwarranted.

A short distance from our hooch, at the far southern edge of the hill, stood a forty-five-foot tower. It had a wooden ladder leading to the top and was sandbagged, two rows thick and about four feet high, all the way around. The roof was covered with a layer of sandbags and was supported by four wooden, telephone-pole–sized posts. The fortified tower could easily accommodate six or seven men at once, without feeling cramped. Located within the tower itself was a .50 caliber machine gun mounted on a stack of the sandbags, a PRC-25 radio, and a PRC-88 field phone. Below the tower, in an underground bunker, was the FDC.

One night, early in my stay at battalion, I was detailed to stand tower watch alone, for the first time. It was a four-hour watch, and I was instructed by a sergeant from the FDC on what my duties were. He told me to report any unusual movement or lights to the FDC and to man the phone. I was still new in country and had no idea of what I was actually supposed to be looking for. His instructions were quite vague, and I neglected to ask for a more precise explanation for fear of appearing stupid. My watch began an hour before nightfall and continued well into darkness. During the early part of my watch, a few officers and NCOs came up into the tower. Some came to visit and others came to check on me.

Lieutenant Jones, a mustang lieutenant—who had worked his way up through the enlisted ranks—was one of those officers who came to check on me. He scared the hell out of me that night when I failed to hear him climb up the ladder. All of a sudden, he was there in the tower with me. He was lanky, bald, in his late forties, and a little *dinky dow*. He always wore a pair of binoculars around his neck when he came up into the tower and would invariably spot what he thought were VC carrying weapons. When someone else looked to confirm his sighting, it usually turned out to be simply farmers carrying hoes or sickles over their shoulders. That night was the first time that I had the distinct pleasure of meeting him. He just stared at me for what seemed like sixty seconds without uttering a sound. Finally, he asked in a low whisper, "Have you seen any activity out there tonight?"

"No, sir!" I answered, shaking my head. Although I really wasn't sure. He said nothing more to me after that and remained in the tower for approximately fifteen minutes peering through his binoculars. Abruptly, he turned toward me and sternly ordered, "Private, make sure anything you spot out there you report in. There's a 1900-hour curfew, and anything out there after that is in a free fire zone. Is that clear?"

"Yes, sir!" I instantly responded.

"Good," he muttered, as he stepped back onto the ladder to leave.

The third hour into my watch I observed a dim light flickering way out in the darkness, but was unsure as to what it was. I watched it for a few minutes before reporting it, as I was instructed. Then I picked up the hand phone and depressed the rubber button on the side three times, causing the phone on the other end to ring. I heard a statically enshrouded voice in the earpiece answer, "Fire Directional Center!"

I relayed to him exactly what it was that I had observed. "What direction?" he asked very nonchalantly, almost as though I was annoying him.

"I don't know! It's directly in front of me."

"All right . . . look in the left hand corner on top of the sandbags. . . . Do you see a flat board with an arrow there?"

"Yes."

"Okay . . . point the arrow at the lights and read off the numbers under it in mils."

"Okay, hold on one." I put down the phone because the wire wouldn't reach; then I pointed the arrow at the lights, noted the reading, and returned to the phone. "Hello, you there?. . . . It reads four thousand two hundred and fifty mils."

"Okay. What's the distance?"

I didn't know. It was awfully dark and extremely difficult to tell. "About one thousand meters?" I hesitantly guessed.

Within minutes of hanging up the phone, both arty and mortars began firing. At that same moment, my heart instantly went into palpitations. I was scared out of my wits, but still managed to watch where the rounds were hitting. I was somewhat surprised for a second that my estimation of the distance was correct. The rounds appeared to have landed directly upon the target.

Several minutes later, three officers climbed into the tower. In the darkness it was hard to discern an unfamiliar face, although I knew one of them was Lieutenant Jones, but the others I didn't recognize. They watched for a few seconds with binoculars and then one of them angrily yelled, "Who the hell called this in? That's a ville out there!"

Oh shit! Boy did I screw up! I'm probably gonna go to jail now! I cringed to myself.

I moved as far back into the corner as I could to keep out of their way, scared to death that I was in a world of shit. My eyes stayed affixed on the now burning ville. To the unaided eye it appeared as only a flickering blaze in the far-off distance. Nevertheless, it captivated me as though I was in a trance. Just then I caught part of what Lieutenant Jones was yelling: "There's secondary explosions out there! Look at that! It's probably a VC ville and they were hiding an ammo cache out there, Colonel!"

The colonel coldly remarked, "Yes, there does seem to be some secondaries out there after all, Lieutenant."

Lieutenant Jones quickly got on the phone and conferred with the FDC for a minute or so; then he turned to the officer standing next to him and said with some excitement in his voice, "Major Silkcraft, FDC reports lights were observed out there and they plotted a fire mission on it." The major didn't look at him, but simply nodded in reply.

The colonel still sounded pissed off when he snapped, "Okay! Let's go down to the FDC and see what the hell's going on here."

My heart was still pounding a mile a minute. I didn't know what was going to happen to me. Was it going to be okay because there were secondary explosions? I sure didn't know. I kept asking myself, "Why me?" At any minute I expected them to come back up for me, but no one came.

All the commotion rather quickly settled down, but the remainder of my watch continued to be unbearably nerve-racking. There was no movement or lights anywhere at all. I made sure of that!

When my relief finally arrived, I left as quickly as possible. I went back to my hooch to get some sleep and tried to forget about what had happened. Only I couldn't.

The next day a patrol from Second Platoon went out to reconnoiter the area and found signs of only a few wounded that had obviously been dragged off, a couple of dead chickens, several tunnels leading out of the ville, and the remains of an ammo cache. I was saved! Thank God!

Our guns were very active firing *boo koo* fire missions and were resupplied with ammo many times over. I quickly discovered that what was taught to us in mortar school was not necessarily practiced in actual combat. Rounds were more often than not man-handled, and unopened ammo boxes tossed around as though they were empty. But by the same token, the gun would have to be cleaned each day after morning chow, whether it was fired or not. It was the whole squad's responsibility. Likewise, each evening we ran gun drill before chow, so that it became second nature to us.

I wanted more than anything else to be the A-gunner on our squad; however, the only way that could happen was if the position was open and I was next in line or if I challenged the A-gunner for the position. A strong desire to achieve my goal motivated me. I practiced on the gun whenever I had free time and got my time down pretty quickly. Sergeant Stacker often saw me practicing by myself and lent me a helping hand by pointing out my mistakes. He seemed to have taken a liking to me and the feeling was mutual.

Sergeant Stacker was in his early twenties. If I had to guess, I would have said that he was most likely from New York or Connecticut. He never did say. The only other thing I knew about him was that when he finished his tour in Nam, he was going to be reassigned to drill instructor school at Parris Island, South Carolina. In my opinion, he would make a damn good DI!

In between work details and my self-imposed gun drill, I nearly always found time to write to my girl friend, Noreen, and to my family. When I wrote home for the first time, I included my address for them to write back: 81s, H&S Co., 3rd Batallion, 7th Marines, 1st Mar. Div. FPO, San Francisco, Calif. 96602. Each time I wrote, I would write to someone different. I was extremely anxious to receive my first letter from home and to find out what was happening back in the World. Letters were very important to me; they were a little piece of home. I also wrote to John's folks, asking them to forward my address to John and to send me his address as soon as they heard from him. I wrote to Noreen most often, almost every day—sometimes more. Everyone in Nam had a girl back home, but some never wrote back. Without exception, everyone lived for mail call. The red mail bag always brought perfumed letters, care packages, or tidings from home. We didn't have stamps to post letters, thus, I enjoyed being able to write FREE in the upper right hand corner of the envelope. I felt as though it was a privilege well deserved.

Since I joined the Marine Corps, I had always been lucky and managed to skate mess duty. Finally, my luck ran out and I was detailed to the chow hall for a week. It wasn't as bad as I thought it would be. I had always pictured myself peeling potatoes or washing pots. Well, the peeling potatoes became a reality, but I steered well clear of the pots. I spent hours one day sitting in front of a big pot of starchy water, along with two other guys, peeling spuds. Most of the time I was assigned to the fruit bar in the officers' mess. The best part was getting to sample the fruit. I loved sliced pineapple. One particular day, I must have eaten half a can before I realized it, and the mess sergeant chewed my ass out. All he kept saying was, "Jesus Christ, half the can's gone! What the hell's the matter with you?"

After my first day on mess duty, I was more than ready to go back to the hooch and relax; however, the mess sergeant had other ideas. He ordered me to get my gear and report back for hole watch at the chow hall that night. There was no way that I was going to stand hole watch guarding the damn chow hall all night, especially after just pulling mess duty, without putting up a fight. Fuck him! I thought to myself in a flash. I immediately responded, "I can't, Sarge! I have gun watch!" It was the only thing I could think of to say on the spur of the moment.

Unfortunately he called my bluff and contacted Sergeant Stacker to straighten it out. I couldn't hear his conversation from where I was standing, but if his facial expression was any indication, I was in a world of shit! He slammed down the receiver and stormed back to where I was waiting. With a snarl he reluctantly informed me by shouting, "You don't have to stand hole watch. Go back and report to your gun squad instead." I was taken aback and completely puzzled, but I left before he changed his mind.

On my way back to our area, I tried to hash it out in my mind. The only conclusion that made any sense was that Sergeant Stacker had confirmed my story—but I didn't know why. I gathered all the courage I could muster and reported to Sergeant Stacker at the FDC hooch. I stood there poised to bear the consequences, but to my further surprise he showed no concern and made no mention at all of the call. He merely acknowledged that I was back. Finding his reaction quite unexpected, I shrugged it off until I got back to the hooch. When I mentioned it to Lou I found out, to my great relief, that eighty-ones were exempt from standing hole watch while assigned to mess duty. No wonder the mess sergeant was so pissed!

Oliver Cannis had arrived at battalion with Harvey and I and was assigned to the other gun squad. He was a well-educated, easygoing, yet uncommonly witty, dark-skinned black from the Virgin Islands. I took an immediate liking to him.

Almost from the first day, it became a routine for Oliver and I to volunteer for the morning road sweep from battalion to a small compound across the river from An Hoa, named Phu Loc-Six (An Hoa was an air strip that had been privately owned at one point in the past by a wealthy Vietnamese and was utilized by the U.S. military.) Each day two road sweeps left the battalion hill to check the roads for mines and for booby traps placed there by the Viet Cong during the night. One of the road sweeps went to Phu Loc-Six and the other half way to Da Nang. The Da Nang sweep was met by another road sweep, which originated at Da Nang. No military traffic was allowed over the roads before they were swept clean. Two marines walked point, followed by two others with mine detectors. A squad of grunts follwed, with Oliver and I bringing up the rear, as rear security. We did this regularly, at least two or three times a week.

One morning, Oliver suggested that he and I walk point as a change of pace. I was totally against it and made it abundantly clear: "What are you crazy? If you want to, go right ahead! But you're going to do it alone, because there's no way in hell I'm going to walk point with you."

He ineffectively argued that it was safe: "Nothing has been found for weeks out there!" I wouldn't give in and the road sweep went out with us as rear security.

As it turned out a mine was found one hundred meters out from the gate at Phu Loc-Six. I turned to Oliver and said sarcastically, "And you wanted to walk point today, huh?" Everyone took cover and the mine was blown with C-4. Without further incident, we completed the sweep and were transported back on the first truck out.

A week later, Oliver and I volunteered for the Da Nang road sweep for the first time. This particular sweep was a little longer than we were used to. On this sweep we walked rear security as usual, but unlike the situation on the Phu Loc-Six sweeps, we were followed by many of the local villagers as we went along.

Tensions were exceptionally high, especially when walking rear security. One always had to expect the unexpected. The villagers were quite eager for us to finish and thus had to be continually kept back. There was one particular military-aged Vietnamese, dressed in civies and walking a bike. He was only annoying at first, but he soon drew my close attention and suspicion. He had a deviously frozen smile on his face and kept edging his way up to us. I had to tell him to *didi mow* more than once, but he repeatedly ignored my requests. Finally, I became pissed off. I ordered him to *dung lai* and had to resort to pointing my M-16 in his face before he finally got the message. His smile quickly disappeared and he backed off about ten meters. He kept his distance from then on.

Oliver and I were about forty meters behind the main body of the road sweep when we were signaled to stop. It was time to take a break. I removed my helmet, wiped the sweat from my forehead with the back of my wrist, and then sat on my helmet near the middle of the road. With one hand grasping my M-16 cradled on my lap, I kept a sharp eye out all around us. I sat facing in the direction that we had been moving toward and Oliver stood facing the direction we had just traveled from.

With sudden urgency, Oliver motioned toward our rear. As I swung around I caught a rapid movement a considerable distance down the road with my peripheral vision. It was a water buffalo galloping directly toward us at full speed! I nearly shit when I spotted it. I had heard rumors that guys had emptied entire magazines into one with little effect. I also knew that water buffalos hated American GIs; something about our scent irritated them.

I quickly surveyed the lay of the land. Rice paddies separated by dikes stretched for several hundred meters west of the road. About fifty meters behind our present position, a narrow path forked off the road and extended far out into the rice paddies. Nervously, I shouted to Oliver, "If that water buffalo passes the path back there, I'm going to empty my sixteen into its fuckin' head!"

I was standing and had already sighted in on its broad forehead, directly in the center of its two large horns. But at that distance it was a very small target. Sweat was streaming down my face and I was trembling with fear. I could barely hold the rifle steady as the water buffalo rapidly closed the distance. Suddenly, Oliver shouted, "Oh shit!" I jumped a foot. "It's not gonna turn off! Let him have it, Ski!"

Every muscle in my body was frozen in position as I began to gradually squeeze the trigger. At the same time, I began to pray that eighteen rounds of ammo would be sufficient to stop it. At the very last second, I watched the water buffalo through my sight veer off the road and onto the path. I slowly let out a big sigh of relief and eased the weapon down to my side with one hand. I turned toward Oliver expecting him to have something witty to say, but instead caught him momentarily speechless and as white as a sheet. He finally managed a smile and murmured, "That was a little too close for comfort."

After that frightening episode, it took a few minutes before my heartbeat slowed to its normal rate. By that time, we were given the signal to move out. We continued along the road until we linked up with the sweep from Da Nang; then we headed back again to battalion.

The next night, as dusk turned into darkness, three patrols silently moved off the hill. They were instructed to set up ambush sites at predetermined coordinates northeast of our hill, near Liberty Bridge. The most recent repairs on the bridge had been completed by the engineers that day, and the gooks were expected to try to burn it again. As a result, both of our gun squads were on standby that night.

Since it was not our turn as primary gun that night, our squad was allowed to attend the flick being shown at the special services hooch. Only a short distance away from our gun pit, about twenty marines gathered around the outside of the special services hooch to watch *Barefoot in the Park* shown on a white sheet nailed to the side of the hooch. The flick had only begun when the patrols sprang their ambushes on what turned out to be a reinforced company of NVA. The resulting encounter sounded like all hell had broken loose. As everyone scattered, we ran back to our gun pit and a fierce fight started to rage. Within minutes of the initial contact, the gooks pulled back and we began dropping rounds on their position.

Just prior to the impact of our first two rounds, only sporadic AK fire and an occasional mortar thump could be heard emanating from the wood line, due west of the ambush sites. Subsequently, the rounds landed right on target.

A frantic patrol leader out at the ambush site called for us to fire ten more rounds for effect. Our gun fired those as rapidly as possible. Simultaneously, a single round of illumination was fired by the other gun. I heard the last round of HE explode as the illumination popped, lighting the entire area over the ambush sites. A short burst of machine gun fire was heard; then, a silence quelled the air. We stood by while the other gun continued to fire illumination for nearly an hour before the word came to secure the guns.

When the patrols returned in the morning, they reported a body count of nineteen and brought back several AK-47s. They were lucky in the fact that they had suffered only one wounded and none mortally. It was a long night, but they managed to keep the bridge intact and disrupt the enemy's movement. The results of the ambush made the colonel happier than a pig in shit.

There was a considerable amount of scuttlebutt circulating around the hill that the battalion was moving lock, stock, and barrel, north to the Khe Sanh. The marines there had been fending off fierce ground and artillery attacks unleashed by the combined efforts of the 325C and the 304th NVA divisions since early February. They were virtually under siege and we were supposed to relieve a battalion of the Third Division. The rumors spread around the hill like wildfire. Even the battalion mail clerk was preparing things for the move. Fortunately for us, in spite of the scuttlebutt and all of the preparations, the move never materialized.

I hadn't heard from John yet and often wondered how he was holding up, with all that was happening up around Khe Sanh. All the reports that I had heard certainly indicated that things were pretty hot and heavy up there. I only knew for sure that John was with the Third Division, but I strongly suspected that Khe Sanh was where he ended up.

A month had gone by since I had arrived in country, and I decided that I was finally proficient enough to challenge the A-gunner. Unfortunately, Lou had just recently assumed the position of A-gunner when Banks rotated. Reluctantly, I had to make my challenge against Lou. That caused me some anguish since I didn't want Lou to take it as a personal attack on our friendship. Nevertheless, I informed both Sergeant Stacker and Lou of my intentions. The next day at gun drill I officially challenged him for the position of A-gunner.

The rules were clear and simple: the best out of three tries. The one with the quickest time for setting the gun up—so that it was ready to be fired—was the winner. Since I made the challenge, I went first.

In a matter of minutes it was all over. I had the better time by several seconds and became the new A-gunner. I was ecstatic with having accomplished my goal, but unduly worried about Lou. He was a little down on himself because I had beaten him decisively. It was our friendship that was most important, but it didn't suffer because of my victory. We merely reversed our positions in the squad and from that point on established a greater respect for one another.

One quiet afternoon, I was in the tower with Lou and Harvey when Lieutenant Jones showed up with his binoculars. He said little and slowly began to scan the distant rice paddies. A few seconds later, without warning, he shoved the binoculars into Lou's hands and pointed toward one distant section. "Do you see those three gooks out there with helmets and packs?" he asked in an excited whisper. Lou raised the binoculars and searched in vain but spotted no one. "No, sir. I don't see them, Lieutenant," he answered.

Lieutenant Jones was insistent that they were there. He rang the phone to the FDC and ordered them to prepare for a fire mission. Next he went to the .50 caliber machine gun and struggled to pull back the bolt. After he tried a few times and discovered he couldn't budge it, he mumbled under his breath, "Damn it! It must be jammed." He paused for a second, then ordered Harvey to see what was wrong with it. Harvey positioned himself behind the gun to get the best leverage, and with very little effort pulled the bolt fully back and allowed it to slam home with a loud whack. Then, with a devilish grin, he turned toward the lieutenant and sarcastically said, "It's fixed, sir."

I had to look away from Harvey and had to bite my lip in order to keep from laughing. When I looked in Lou's direction, he was also having a difficult time trying not to laugh out loud. As Lieutenant Jones stood with his back toward the .50 caliber, Harvey continued mocking him by making a rapid hand gesture—indicating that the lieutenant was a jerk-off.

Suddenly, a voice from below the tower called out, "JONES . . . GET THE HELL OUT OF THAT TOWER!" I leaned over and recognized an officer from the FDC bunker standing at the bottom of the ladder looking upward. He held his hands cupped over his mouth and again yelled, "Did you hear me, Jones?" The lieutenant didn't answer immediately, but after a brief exchange of shouts he reluctantly climbed down from the tower.

Lieutenant Jones was one officer who, aside from his misguided and unorthodox ideas, never ceased to amaze me. Be that as it may, credit should be given where it is due; he surely demonstrated a persistent quality in his eccentric behavior.

A perfect illustration was the time he dreamed up the cock-eyed idea of using two tanks, one on each side of the tower, with their sights synchronized so that they could combine fire on a selected target. He somehow convinced the battalion commander to let him demonstrate his idea. Once again, it was my misfortune to be on tower watch at the precise time the demo was scheduled.

Lieutenant Jones strolled up to the tower wearing a tank helmet fitted with a miniature radio that was pre-set to the tank's frequency. The radio enabled him to have direct communication with both tanks from the tower. He spent the better part of an hour, prior to the demo, trying to coordinate and position the two tanks. Despite the radio-equipped helmet, he made frequent trips up and down the tower and from tank to tank before he was satisfied.

The colonel and Major Silkcraft arrived in the tower promptly at 1400 hours; however, they were kept waiting while the lieutenant scurried about making last minute adjustments. It soon became evident that the colonel was annoyed by the delay. With mounting exasperation, he leaned over the side of the tower and shouted, "Lieutenant, I rotate in three months! Let's get this goddamn demonstration in gear!" The veins in the colonel's neck were still bulging when he turned to the major and complained, "I don't know why I allowed him to talk me into this."

"He must've caught you in one of your rare good moods," the major quipped with a slight smirk.

"That's real funny, Major," he retorted.

When the tanks were finally adjusted to the lieutenant's satisfaction, he sprinted back to the tower. The target was preselected:

a wood line about five hundred meters out. With the colonel's permission he gave the command to fire. Both tanks let loose simultaneously. The shells were fired with a thunderous cloud of gray smoke. The resulting concussion shook the tower as well as the ville directly below us. When the smoke dissipated it was obvious that the target was destroyed and the demo seemingly a success! Lieutenant Jones puffed with pride as he was complimented by his superiors.

Ironically, though, his success was short-lived when the colonel received a message minutes later, indicating that the village honcho had violently complained about the explosions. Apparently the inside of his hooch had nearly been destroyed by the concussions. Needless to say, the colonel flew into a rage and ordered Lieutenant Jones to shit-can his idea and remove the tanks. The final blow came when the colonel further banished him from the tower.

In spite of my initial and sobering encounter with the tower, I became oddly attracted to it. I always found myself up there. During the day, the view from the tower was spectacular! From high above, one could gaze out upon the fertile landscape and easily imagine the villages and rice paddies below merging into the tree lines, which abruptly rise into mountains, that in turn seem to almost touch the sky. The geometrically shaped rice paddies reflect the endless parade of passing clouds in their mirrorlike, multicolored waters. Had I not known better, this tranquil scene appeared to have never known war.

At night the setting was strikingly different. The beauty of the villages and rice paddies by day was absorbed and blended into the night. Only the lights from other hills sparkled in the darkness. Distant explosions rumbled and echoed in the darkness. An occasional fire fight would break out and sporadic orange tracers darted from wood line to wood line. Through a starlight scope, darkness turned to a greenish hue. Vietnam was as beautiful from a distance as it was hostile close-up.

At mail call one afternoon, I received two letters; one with an unfamiliar return address. The letter was post marked Astoria, New York, which intrigued me, so I opened it first. The letter began with a brief introduction from John's girl friend, Terry, stating that she was writing to me at the request of John's parents. Her letter sadly explained that John was considered the black sheep of the family and that his parents rightfully assumed that she was much more likely to be written to first than they, so they had asked her to answer the letter that they had received from me. She went on to say that she would write occasionally to keep me posted on how John was doing and included his address. I eventually wrote back, thanking her for her thoughtfulness and told her that I would enjoy receiving an occasional letter.

The other letter was from my parents. Besides a mom's typical concern about her son eatng right and being careful, my mom wrote telling me that she had heard that Juan had arrived home and was rapidly recuperating from his wounds. My letter back assured them that I was taking care of myself just fine and asked them to relay my regards to Juan.

The last couple of stragglers had just made it back from morning chow when Sergeant Stacker walked into our hooch. He came to tell us that all the companies in battalion were swapped around and that our section was to be transferred out to Hill 65 with India Company. The move was to be a permanent one and would take place in three days. He further announced that he and Corporal Lewis would remain at battalion and that we would pick up a new section leader once we arrived at Hill 65. The news was met with mixed reactions, but most of us were glad to be getting out of battalion and away from its overabundance of lifers. It was only because of these career officers and NCOs that one always had to look busy or surely be assigned to a superfluous work detail.

Several changes were made affecting our gun squad in anticipation of the planned move to Hill 65. Vic Tasuello was elevated to squad leader. Ned Synoski, originally from Lima Company, was moved to our gun as the new gunner. Oliver Cannis was also moved to our squad. That brought us up to TO, with Lou as first ammo humper, Harvey as second ammo humper, Oliver as third ammo humper, and a new guy, Andy Brunnell, as fourth ammo humper.

For the next few days, we scrounged, begged, borrowed, and appropriated all the gear we were lacking. We even managed to come up with a few extra items, like rubber ladies and a chow hall field cooler, thanks to Brunnell. Brunnell seemed to possess a knack for finding lost and useful items. He even looked the part—beady eyes and all. Brunnell was born and raised in the back hills of Kentucky and distinctly bore the mannerisms of his country upbringing. He possessed a likable personality and was much wiser than his initial appearance suggested.

It was customary to conspire against a new guy to break his cherry, so to speak, when he was just new in country. So it was with Brunnell. At his first gun drill, Sergeant Stacker sent him to the company supply after he had dropped the gun sight. He was sternly admonished for breaking the cross hairs within the sight and was ordered to draw a bottle of new ones from supply.

The company supply sergeant, being the old salt that he was, immediately realized what was happening when Brunnell appeared requesting the bogus item. Unexpectedly, he too played along with the ruse and sent him clear across the hill to the battalion supply. As it happened, there too he failed to obtain the cross hairs. Greatly distressed, Brunnell returned to the gun pit from his wild goose chase, empty-handed. In a moment of inspiration, he realized that he had been duped and broke the awkwardness of the moment by laughing at himself. He had paid his dues and was accepted as one of the boys, but unwillingly retained the stigma of new guy, until such time as he could relinquish it onto the next cherry!

The air was filled with anticipation on the morning of the

move. Most of everyone's gear was packed the night before and ready to go. Some last minute odds and ends were gathered together and miscellaneous necessities attended to. All but a few rounds of ammo was transported to the staging area by mule earlier that morning; however, the guns were left in place until the very last minute.

Several six-bys noisily arrived at the staging area and were properly positioned to facilitate loading them. Soon, the area became a beehive of activity. In no time at all, the entire company was loaded and ready to move out. The CO's driver maneuvered his jeep along the column of trucks brimming with men and equipment and took his position at the lead. Only after a last minute check was made did our new CO, Capt. Charles Drew, motion our small convoy forward, and we rolled out of battalion.

3. Hill 65

We traveled in a southwesterly direction, away from the battalion hill, and before we knew it, we found ourselves at our new fire base, Hill 65. Like most other hills, it derived its name from its elevation. Compared to battalion, it was a small hill, long and rather narrow at the top, with one end much wider than the other. Several small villes surrounded the base of the hill and a garbage dump was located at the far northern end. A combined action platoon (CAP) unit was situated just to the south, about three hundred meters out.

Our company was assigned the narrower and unoccupied end of the hill. A collection of various size hooches, constructed out of dirt-filled ammo boxes, were scattered about the area. There were two gun pits, flanked by a hooch on each side and an FDC hooch in the middle. A narrow dirt road ran slightly downhill and alongside of them leading out to the point.

My squad was assigned to both the hooch and the gun pit nearest to the point. Directly in front of our hooch and across the road was the shitter. Unfortunately, we paid the price for its convenience—eighty-ones were detailed to clean it! Immediately past our gun pit area was another large hooch. First Platoon claimed it as their's. In the opposite direction, just above the other gun pit, was a tower built on a large mound. Right behind and directly beneath it was an underground bunker that was utilized as the company commander's CP and sleeping quarters. The only access road to the hill itself led to a large open area, between our end of the hill and a set of 105-mm and 155-mm artillery batteries, which were already stationed there. The previous rifle company had vacated the hill prior to our arrival. We were virtually it, as far as security of the hill was concerned.

Waiting for us when we arrived was the new section leader, Sergeant Mailer and his assistant, Corporal Hanks. Also with them was the RO, Lance Corporal Bailey, whose nickname was Slack.

Sergeant Mailer walked around with a slight limp in his right leg. When questioned, he related the story of being wounded by enemy fire during a fire fight while out on his last operation. But in contrast to his dubious version, scuttlebutt had it that he was fragged by one of his own men. In my mind, the latter was the more likely scenario. A significant revelation if true!

Personally, I developed a strong distaste for Sergeant Mailer right from the beginning. His moody disposition, coupled with his extremely arrogant personality were the prominent reasons. Aside from these less than admirable qualities, there was something disturbing about him that I just couldn't put my finger on. Perhaps it was the pugnacious look on his face that was the elusive factor. Whatever it was, it became quite evident early on that Sergeant Mailer tried in earnest to fulfill the role of command but fell hopelessly short of gaining the desired respect and trust of his men. He lacked all of the positive qualities that Sergeant Stacker possessed.

It seemed to me that the only person who did get along with him was Corporal Hanks. Hanks, too, I had a hard time stomaching, although it was for totally different reasons. Primarily it was because he acted like an asshole most of the time. It was no wonder that he and Sergeant Mailer got along so well!

Corporal Hanks was a second generation Mexican-American, who habitually raved about southern California. He had a severely pockmarked face, thick jet-black hair, and was blind as a bat without his glasses.

Then there was Slack, the oddball of the trio, who was more than aptly named for his lack of motivation. Although his personal appearance left a lot to be desired, he was unlike some whose personal hygiene begged to be improved. More often than not, he could be found napping somewhere quietly and usually accomplishing as little work as possible.

After dropping off our personal gear in the hooch, the first thing that I checked was the ammo bunker. I wanted to see how much ammo there was, because we had only brought along a few rounds. Each type of ammo was stored in its own separate bunker. There was plenty of HE and a good supply of illumination; however, we were in desperate need of WP. Our gun pit was about twelve feet in diameter and enclosed by two rows of sandbags, about two feet high, with the ammo bunker situated so that it opened into the gun pit.

When we were ready to seat the base plate, it was placed in the center of the pit on several sandbags. Then the tube with the bipod attached was placed into the base plate. The elevation was cranked all the way up and the bipod pulled in close. One round of illumination was fired to seat the base plate into the ground. Sometimes a second round was needed. But with fifty-two thousand pounds of pressure per square inch, it didn't need many to seat it. We used illumination, because we had to fire straight up. It was quite obvious why HE and WP rounds weren't used—no one wanted to be a hero and drop explosive rounds on themselves.

After we set the base plate, we bore-sighted the tube and laid in the four aiming stakes. Two at twelve o'clock and two at six o'clock about six feet apart. The two at twelve o'clock were placed on the opposite side of the road, next to a small bunker. The remaining two were placed much closer to the gun pit. This was necessitated by the close proximity of the gun pit to the edge of the hill. The gun was then cleaned and covered with a poncho.

With both guns in place, we checked the hand phones between the gun pits and the FDC. They were found to work just fine.

There was also a PRC-88 field phone in each hooch connected to the FDC. It was used to sound a fire mission. It rang twice if we had to fire, which saved us valuable time answering the phone.

We spent the rest of the day getting our hooch squared away. It was a disaster area and had to be thoroughly cleaned out. I claimed the bunk in the left-hand corner for myself and constructed a makeshift desk out of several ammo boxes to put next to it. In it, I stored some of my smaller gear and the rest went under my rack.

The hooch was about twenty-five feet wide by eighteen feet deep, while the inside measured only slightly over six feet in height. It had a sandbagged roof, tar paper covering its dirt-filled ammo box walls, a single door with a short overhang, supported by two engineering stakes, and a small platform in front. The inside smelled of an odor, much the same as an old dank musty cellar. Two windows near the roof, one on each side, supplied the sorely needed cross-ventilation. Unlike our hooch at battalion, it had no electricity and, consequently, no lights. Candles or flashlights were our only source of light after dark.

We were all getting hungry, which prompted Vic to break out a case of C-rats. The one I grabbed was marked MEAL, COMBAT, INDIVIDUAL—BEEF, SPICED W/SAUCE—B-3 UNIT.

After carefully constructing a stove out of the cracker can, I opened the beef with a C-rat opener and proceeded to cook it, using a heat tab. I spread the crackers with a little jam and ate them along with the beef. The can of pears that came with the meal, I saved for later. Next, I opened the foil packet from inside the box, took out the hot cocoa mix, sugar, and cream packets, and mixed them each into a canteen cup full of hot water. It wasn't the greatest, but it sufficed!

Later, I was able to perfect the hot cocoa recipe to a degree where it was quite tasty. The waterproof matches, the two chicklets of gum, and the shit paper I placed in my pockets and gave the Winston cigarettes to Harvey. I rarely used the salt and pepper, but saved them anyway.

Oliver had tried in vain to trade his turkey loaf for something else—like pears or peaches—but no one wanted to trade with him, including me. As we were finishing up, Hanks came by and told Vic that Sergeant Mailer had called a meeting in twenty minutes at the FDC hooch.

Having nothing to do while Vic was at the meeting, I decided to sprawl out on my rack and relax. Ned followed my lead, and before long, the entire squad was doing the same.

Lying there, I began to reflect on my feelings and emotions since I had arrived in country. I soon realized that they were many and complex: fear, anger, uncertainty, sadness, fatigue, pride, hatred, a strange feeling of contentment, a strong sense of duty, apathy, and sometimes sympathy for the innocent civilians. All of them seemed to be scrambled together, continually tossed about, and then one or more prominently emerging, much like dice before they are thrown out on the table—where the result of each throw is unpredictable. Having to grapple with such a bevy of emotions left me confused and despondent. I despised my inability to cope and chose to ignore them instead.

A short while later, Vic returned to the hooch with orders that he knew he would balk about. He told us that the CO had received information that our hill would probably get hit with a ground attack, either that night or within the next night or two. "That means we will have to man the bunkers around our end of the hill, all night and probably for the next couple of nights, too. It also means that we'll possibly be in them for a week. . . . No one fuckin' knows for sure yet," Vic went on to explain.

Quite out of character, I was the first to speak out. "Shit! The fuckin' gooks are fuckin' with us already . . . and we only got here!" I angrily shouted. "I'd rather be on the gun if we're going to get hit!"

"Me too!" Ned seconded my statement.

Everyone else was in agreement, too. "I have no say in the

matter—that's what the captain wants! What the fuck do you want from me?" countered Vic. "I'm just passing on the orders . . . that's all." I was surprised at my sudden outburst and knew that I had said more than enough already. A sudden silence drifted through the hooch.

"We know. It's just that the whole thing sucks!" consoled Lou.

Numerous strands of barbed wire ran the entire length of the hill on both sides. Directly behind the wire, on the west side, was a three-foot-wide trench, four and a half feet deep. Every thirty meters or so, along the trench line, a bunker was located.

Ned and I had a look around and chose the bunker nearest to our gun pit, on the west side. In it was a small ledge dug into the back wall, just the right height to sit on comfortably, apparently fashioned by a previous occupant. The others paired off, selected their positions, and gathered their gear. Together, we prepared for a long night on hole watch.

The men in each bunker, on the west side of the hill, were issued a LAAW in addition to their own weapons. Those on the east side were issued Claymore mines to set up. There was only sufficient room to use the Claymores on the east side.

A LAAW was a light antitank weapon and a Claymore was a fragmentation mine used against infantry. Just in case, I took two M-26 grenades, as did most everyone else. I also brought along the can of pears that I had saved earlier, and Ned brought some crackers and peanut butter. We both had our canteens full of water as well. Since I had to turn in my M-16 for a .45 automatic when I made A-gunner, and Ned carried one too, we were both issued M-16s by the company gunnery sergeant.

After the third night of no activity, we decided to switch positions the next night. This time, Lou and I shared a bunker together on the east side of the hill. We had set up our Claymores in front of our bunker and settled in for another long and quiet night.

An hour or so after dark, we heard someone approach our

bunker from the road behind us. We both were relatively sure that it was a friendly and strongly suspected that it was the company gunny checking up on us. But whoever it was hadn't given the password. As the sound of footsteps got closer, Lou sharply pulled back the bolt on his '16 and let it slam home. Its very distinct sound echoed loudly inside the bunker. He drew a bead on the steadily approaching figure and whispered, "Halt! Or I'll blow you the fuck away!"

The footsteps stopped cold and a voice frantically called out from the darkness, "It's me . . . Gunny! Don't shoot!"

Lou turned to me, smiled and whispered, "I suppose the asshole got the message." We listened for a short time as he hurriedly moved off. He didn't come back to our bunker for the rest of the night.

Lou took the first two-hour watch, and before I knew it, he was waking me for mine. I tried to work the soreness out of my back by stretching a little, but the dampness seemed to have worked its way into my back muscles pretty good. I paused for a second to clear my head and then whispered, "Anything happening out there?"

"No. It's quiet," he answered, trying to stifle a yawn. Lou sat down beside me, snuggled himself into the corner, and instantly fell asleep.

My watch wasn't half over when things started jumping. From the bunker to our right an M-60 machine gun opened up, blasting wildly down the side of hill. Without warning, a grenade exploded with a flash, spewing red hot shrapnel in all directions. Then, someone else further down the line started firing, too. As I yelled for Lou to wake up, a hand flare popped and lit up our side of the hill. Its light only lasted a few seconds, but long enough to expose the enemy's movement. "I can't see a fuckin' thing out there!" I said to Lou, desperately straining in the darkness.

Jumping up, Lou shouted, "What the hell's going on?" It was merely a rhetorical question; he knew full well what was happening. The problem was that neither one of us could make out what was being shot at. I was taking no chances and had my fingers on the plunger of my Claymore, ready to blast the first gook dumb enough to climb the hill. Behind us and in the distance, we heard someone yelling, "Cease Fire! Cease Fire!"

Then, just as suddenly as it began, it was over. A piercing silence swept the warm air of the night. I remained motionless. Only my eyes scoured an arc across the line of sight from our bunker. Other than an occasional wisp of cordite, all evidence of the brief fire fight had vanished into the obscurity of the landscape. Fending off fatigue, Lou and I remained awake for the rest of the night, staring out at the shadows anxiously awaiting daybreak.

At first light we wearily collected our gear and secured the bunker. As Lou and I tottered out to retrieve our Claymores, we found that they had been turned around and were facing our bunker! I nearly shit at the thought of firing them and being blown away by my own hand. Then it struck me: a gook had to have crawled up to them and turned them around. We had placed them out there ourselves the night before. There was just no other answer! Neither one of us had seen or heard anyone out in the wire during the night. That's when Lou went into a rage. He completely lost his composure and was screaming uncontrollably. "Those fuckin' gooks turned our Claymores around at us!" He kept yelling it over and over again. It took nearly half the day before he calmed down enough to stop yelling about it.

Captain Drew finally decided to secure the perimeter watch after the fifth day. Apparently S2 had some bad information.

We received more good news when we were told that the captain had made arrangements with the arty battery's CO and their mess sergeant, so that our company could eat at their chow hall. The only hitch was that the company had to supply a man each week for mess duty. After eating C-rats for five days straight, it was a welcomed change.

For the next couple of weeks, things became somewhat

routine. We made some minor changes and improvements on the gun pits and ammo bunkers. We replaced a lot of torn sandbags—a tedious chore that no one liked. We cleaned the guns in the morning, ran gun drill in the evening, and fired fire missions in between it all.

One day, Lou and I were filling sandbags to be used in rebuilding the side of the ammo bunker. While sitting on the ground next to each other, Lou dug up a large rock and, without looking, casually tossed it a few feet away. It bounced toward the trip wire of a large ship flare, one of many scattered along the perimeter of the hill. As it happened, I was looking in that particular direction at the moment he threw the rock. I watched it tumble onto the trip wire in terror, realizing that the flare would ignite in seconds. Dropping my E-tool in a panic, I screamed at Lou, grasping his shirt, and stumbled backward as I dragged him clear. I knew that he was unaware of what was about to happen—and for that matter—that he had caused it. A split second later, the incendiary grenade inside the flare ignited, spewing out its white-hot contents like a miniature volcano. The resulting display was nowhere near as illuminating as it would have been had it been dark; however, the accidental fireworks had not gone unnoticed by the company gunny. He had a few choice words to spew out himself! Unfortunately, we were the recipients of his fury.

Two new guys arrived with the first resupply truck out to our hill. One of them, named Al Butler, was assigned to our gun squad, and the other, Ken Randy, was our new FO. Al was from Nevada and Ken was from Pennsylvania, near Pittsburgh. Al was thin, wore glasses, and had a good sense of humor. Ken, on the other hand, was a little chunky, had a double chin, and a rummy nose.

With the arrival of a new ammo humper, Harvey subsequently moved to the other gun squad, becoming their first ammo humper.

Once the new guys were settled in and introduced around, we

put them right to work helping us break out the ammo. There were several pallets of ammo dropped off by the resupply truck that had to be broken out and stored away. Each box contained three canisters and was sealed with two metal straps and a latch, which had to be cut open. Experience found that the easiest way to open a box was to stand on it, facing the front, and strike it with an E-tool on the metal straps, thereby breaking them off. With some practice, a box could be opened with only three blows.

Once the ammo boxes were all emptied and the rounds were taken out of the canisters, the packing removed, and the rounds replaced, the canisters were stacked in the ammo bunker. This took a few hours to complete, depending on how much ammo we were resupplied with. We usually kept several hundred rounds on hand and about thirty HE and WP canisters opened and ready to fire.

The illumination rounds came in metal canisters, which had to be opened with a key, similar to a canned ham. They were a bitch to open if the strip on one broke. Guys were always cutting themselves with it. The canister then had to be opened by using a C-rat opener. It became very tiresome opening more than one or two in this fashion. Someone finally wrote home for a mechanical can opener. At least that made the chore a little bit easier.

We took turns alternating gun duty each night. The squad that was on duty would fire all fire missions and H&I's, unless we got hit, then both squads were on the guns. No matter which squad had duty, one of its men stood radio watch in the FDC hooch. Slack would take the watch until midnight, then the duty squad took over. Watches were two hours each and ended at 0600 hours. If a fire mission was called in, the man on watch would immediately be relieved to take his place on the gun.

The call sign for our section was Whiskey India. The battalion section was Whiskey Mike and the section at Phu Loc-Six was Whiskey Lima. At the beginning and then again at the completion of each radio watch, we would have to check on or off the net. Eighty-ones operated on a different frequency than India Company itself; however, to contact them, all that needed to be done was simply turn the dial to their frequency and call.

It was mid-May and about six weeks after we arrived on the hill. It was a particularly hot night and my squad had gun duty. I had just been awakened by Oliver for my watch. "What time is it?" I asked.

"Zero one forty-five. Are you sure you're up?" Oliver whispered.

"Yeah, I'm awake. I'll be right over." Oliver left the hooch and went back.

I lay there for a few moments, rubbing the sleep from my eyes. I could barely make out anything inside the hooch, other than the moonlight coming from the doorway. The hooch was pitch black. I heard a noise in the far corner. It was Lou tossing in his sleep. I sat up, put my cover on, felt around for my flashlight and writing paper, slipped into my boots—not bothering to tie them—and shuffled out the door. Outside it was extremely quiet. All that could be heard was my boots clopping as I staggered along. I walked around the back of the hooch toward FDC and stopped to take a leak first. All of a sudden, I had a funny feeling as though someone was watching me! Nervously, I glanced around, but no one was there. When I was finished relieving myself, I stumbled past our gun pit and into the FDC.

The FDC hooch had two rooms with a wall dividing them. One room was a little larger than the other. A blanket was nailed over the doorway to provide some privacy, because the larger outer room was filled with bunks. The other room was the actual FDC. It had a table with the plotting board, a PRC-25 radio, two PRC-88 field phones, and two hand phones hanging from it. A single light bulb hung above the table and dimly lit the room. Along the far wall was Sergeant Mailer's and Corporal Hanks's bunks, which were both equipped with green mosquito netting.

I walked in, still shuffling my feet, when Oliver said quietly, "You made it I see."

"Yeah, I'm here," I replied with a big yawn. "Go get some sleep."

He picked up the book he had been reading and left, saying, "See you in the morning, Ski."

I nodded, still half asleep, and sat down in front of the table. Staring at the mike for a few seconds, trying to clear the cobwebs, I slowly picked it up and checked in on the net. "Whiskey India to Whiskey Mike, over."

"Come in, Whiskey India," answered the battalion RO.

"Permission to enter the net? Over."

"Roger, Whiskey India. Permission granted."

I picked up a *Playboy* magazine from the stack under the table. Flipping through the pages, I read some of the articles and paused to drool over the centerfold. Miss April had the most luscious looking body and a big set of tits! I was getting awfully horny.

► Outside in the distance, I thought I heard some small arms fire. I strained to listen, but heard nothing more. I checked some of the other frequencies on the radio, but no one seemed to be transmitting. Consequently, I figured it was my imagination and went back to reading.

Just as I did, there was a loud explosion! With that, I jumped up and yelled to Sergeant Mailer, who was asleep in his bunk, "Hey, Sarge! Sarge, we're taking incoming!"

He immediately awoke and shouted, "Go on. Go tell 'em to get on the gun!"

I dashed out and ran around our gun pit to the doorway of our hooch. Along the way it sounded like several mortars landed halfway up the side of the hill, behind the shitter. I stood in the doorway for less than a second, screaming, "FIRE MISSION! FIRE MISSION!" as loudly as I could.

Just as I turned toward the gun pit, a round hit directly behind the shitter across the road, spraying shrapnel everywhere. I heard it penetrating the corrugated metal back wall. Almost in the same instant, chunks of it whizzed by my head. I was too petrified to think—I just reacted! The distance was about twenty-five feet from the hooch to our gun pit, and I must have made it there within two strides. I dove over the sandbags and completed a forward roll into the pit.

Seconds later, as I uncovered the gun in preparation to fire, the rest of the squad bounded into the gun pit behind me. Only the new guy had a flak jacket on. The others, including myself, hardly ever wore them on the gun. They only hindered our movement, and speed was extremely important. A few seconds could mean someone's life. We prided ourselves on being quick and accurate.

I didn't know who called it in, but we got a fire mission. Vic picked up the gun pit phone and relayed the information from the FDC to Ned and I. "Two o'clock. . . . Deflection: one—one—two—fiver. . . . Elevation: eleven hundred. . . . Two rounds HE: charge four. . . . Fire when up!"

Ned picked up the bipod, swung it toward two o'clock and planted it firmly in the dirt. I placed a sandbag at the foot of the bipod to keep it steady. Ned then set the gun sight to the correct deflection and elevation and sighted in on the red and white aiming stakes. He checked to see that both the deflection and elevation bubbles were level, made a slight adjustment in elevation, then shouted, "I'm up!"

As he was setting up the gun, the others were preparing the HE rounds with the correct charges. Lou stood next to me and handed me the first round. I checked it to see if the safety pin was removed and that the correct charge was on the round. In the darkness, this was done by feel. I held the round poised above the tube as Ned told me he was up; then I called out "STAND BY!" and guided the fins into the muzzle of the tube and gave it a gentle downward push. A split second later, Lou handed me the second round. Immediately, after the first was out, I dropped it down, too. We heard the rounds hit—two thuds in quick succession!

Vic passed on a slight correction in deflection ordered by the

FDC, and we fired five more rounds of HE for effect. Again we heard the rounds exploding, this time sounding like the rumble of distant thunder. It was the only sound we heard. We stood around the gun waiting to fire again, but were soon given the word to secure. Whatever it was that was happening out there, it was apparently over for now.

I spent a considerable amount of time in the tower at night, shooting the shit with Ken and Al. It seemed like no matter what topic it was that we were talking about, we always managed to get around to swapping stories about home. It became sort of a ritual for the three of us, and because of it, we came to be very close friends. Since Ken was the FO, it was part of his job to be in the tower whenever he was on the hill. We were there simply keeping each other company and passing the time away.

The tower was sort of a squatty looking thing with sandbags covering the dirt mound that it was perched on. Twelve steps, made of ammo boxes, led to the top of the mound. The tower itself was enclosed by sandbagged walls, four feet high, and had a simple, flat, plywood roof, covered with green camouflage plastic. Inside, it had a large pair of ship binoculars mounted on a pillar in the center of the floor and a PRC-25 radio in one corner.

Second Lieutenant Dayton, who was the artillery battery's FO, often joined us in the tower. He had a premature receding hairline and striking steel-blue eyes that accented a cherublike grin. As far as officers were concernd Lieutenant Dayton was really a down-to-earth type of guy and certainly was no lifer. He preferred that we called him by his first name, which was Bill. That in itself was not the norm, at least not with the officers I knew.

One night, when we were all in the tower, the lieutenant came up with another person. Ken was busy in the corner, going over some map coordinates, as Bill introduced Al and I to the chaplain, Major Millington. The chaplain told us that he had come out to the hill earlier in the day and was making the rounds, talking to everyone. He continued on for a few minutes with some small talk and then moved to the far side of the tower and was engaged in a conversation with Bill. Apparently, Ken didn't hear the introduction and was looking through the binoculars when the chaplain unknowingly stepped in front of him, blocking his view. Ken looked up and sarcastically remarked, "You don't make a very good fuckin' window!" Seemingly unaffected by the language, the chaplain quickly apologized and moved out of his way.

I leaned over and whispered in Ken's ear that he had just eloquently chewed out the chaplain. He didn't believe me though, until after the chaplain had gone, and until Bill and Al confirmed that he was indeed the chaplain. Even in the dark I could tell that Ken's face had turned crimson-red with embarrassment.

The next morning was ushered in with the unmistakable sound of choppers approaching the hill. They were Medivac choppers bringing in several KIAs from three clicks out in the valley, just southwest of our hill. A company of marines were pinned down out there for nearly six hours by a larger NVA force. They suffered numerous casualties. As a result, we were placed on standby as a reactionary force. We were prepared to pull up within a matter of minutes, to be choppered out, and then to be inserted into the area to roust the NVA. We had been on standby for the entire morning when the command came to stand down.

When the tension subsided and I calmed down some, I reflected on the feelings that I had experienced at the LZ, with unloading so many bodies. I felt mostly anger and sadness, both at the same time, because they were Americans, just like me—but they were lying there dead. I pictured the anguish and the hurt that their deaths would bring to their families back home. It made me more certain of my convictions and a little more hostile than I had been before. For sometime after, I had a difficult time erasing their faces from my mind.

The guys in the hooch always gathered aound when someone received a package from home. Etiquette dictated that a package was shared among all present. Of course, it was unwritten, but everyone willingly complied.

I received my first package from home. It was from my folks and was much bigger than I had expected it to be. With great anticipation, I tore off the paper wrapper and pulled open the box. The inside was packed with all kinds of goodies. Popcorn was used as packing around the contents. The very first thing that caught my eye was a white box tied with thin string, which I recognized instantly. It was exactly what I thought it was: bakery-made butter cookies, dipped in chocolate and covered with jimmies—two pounds worth from my grandmother! There were some canned fruits, Kool-Aid packets, two cans of Vienna sausages, some pepperoni, and a few personal items too. I shared everything except the cookies. They were mine and I hoarded them jealously.

Someone started eating the popcorn and found out that it wasn't half bad, even stale. Hastily, we all finished off the packing and washed it down with warm Kool-Aid. It was a treat we all appreciated.

The following night, a fire broke out in the ville, just below the east side of the hill. None of our patrols were involved to our knowledge, and it quickly became apparent that it was not directed toward our hill either. After a few minutes, we realized that the local skivvy house was the focus of the VC attack. The skivvy house employed several boom-boom girls and apparently neglected to pay their taxes, due in rice, to the VC. Within a matter of minutes, the episode was over and the message surely understood.

A gook shop was allowed to operate on our hill and was located at the top of the access road. It was in an ordinary canvas tent, faded to a sun-bleached, mud-brown color. Two wooden posts supported the inside, while many ropes, tied to metal stakes, kept the tent drawn to its proper shape. It was operated by several enterprising villagers, offering various items and services for sale: haircuts, laundry, Coca-Cola, ice, photo albums, et cetera. They were there each morning and had to be off the hill before sunset each day.

This one old papa-san, who rode a rickety old bicycle, was

the lone barber at our gook shop. Considering what he had to work with—an old pair of hand clippers, a pair of scissors, and an ordinary straight razor—he gave a fairly decent haircut. Just the same, I was not very trusting of any Vietnamese handling a potentially dangerous weapon, such as a straight razor, in such close proximity to my throat. Subsequently, when I sat in his chair, I always unholstered my .45 automatic, showed it to him, and placed it on my lap. Somehow I knew the message transcended our language barrier.

I would have my hair cut often and kept it fairly short. Partially due to the heat and also for the ease of keeping it clean, but mainly because the hair on the right side of my head would become singed from the blast of the gun each time we fired.

No matter what it was that one purchased, they always insisted on being paid in MPC and usually tried to pawn off plasters for change. Plasters were Vietnamese currency, which were valued slightly less than their equivalent in MPC.

Attached to the exterior of our hooch was a makeshift shower. It was a wooden stall with a fifty-five gallon drum perched on top, which was painstakingly filled by hand. Many trips to the water bull, located a short distance over the crest of the hill, with two jerry cans each, were necessary to fill it. Lugging a five-gallon can in each hand, filled to the brim and sloshing back and forth was not my idea of a desirable preshower activity. Then again, the acccommodations were not the Waldorf-Astoria either! A simple spigot arrangement controlled the flow of water. On occasion, we had heated water to shower with, thanks to a mysteriously acquired water heater installed in the drum, the type of which was usually found in use only at a chow hall. The shower itself offered little in the way of privacy, for it had no door; however, it did have somewhat of a redeeming value in the way of a breathtaking view off the side of the hill, looking down into the valley.

Like clockwork—you could set your watch to it—the gooks

would harass the CAP unit, just off our hill, every evening at 1830 hours. More often than not, they would lob a few mortars or an occasional RPG into the compound.

More than once, while in the shower, I found myself scampering to the gun pit, with only a green towel wrapped around my waist and sopping wet, because the CAP unit was getting hit and we had to fire.

Fear of the CAP unit being overrun one night prompted the CO to send First Platoon out there to set up on its perimeter. Normally, only a handful of marines and a squad of PF's manned the compound at night. During the day, these same marines would instruct the local villagers on ways to improve their lives through agriculture.

Just as darkness fell, its perimeter was probed at several locations, then everything broke loose. The platoon sergeant called in all kinds of fire missions, some of which came uncomfortably close to their positions. Both of our guns almost continuously fired the entire time, keeping the area well lit with illumination.

A moderate wind had been blowing in our direction, and the white silk parachutes, from the illumination rounds, floated back toward us. During a lull in which our gun was not firing, I was determined to snag one as a souvenir. Suddenly, the wind shifted and it carried them aloft, missing our hill completely. Then, I noticed one coming in much lower than the others. I hopped out of the gun pit and chased it along the barbed wire until it floated down low enough for me to reach it. I must have been a sight. There I was carelessly jumping up along the barbed wire edge of the hill, oblivious to the raging battle in the background, trying to catch hold of a parachute. I did, however, feel a sense of accomplishment when I finally succeeded in nabbing it. (In retrospect, it was a rather foolhardy escapade.)

The NVA's consorted effort to overrun the CAP unit continued for several hours, until an air strike was called in from Da

Nang. Two camouflaged F-4 Phantoms made several thundering, low altitude passes, dropping their ordnance along the wood line. By that time, First Platoon had pulled back their positions into the relative safety of the compound. When the air strike was terminated, the pilots maneuvered their aircraft into position and executed a fly-by over our hill, signaling a successful mission, then headed for home.

The enemy's relentless persistence had been substantially weakened by the air strike. What remained was only sporadic small arms fire. Eventually, that too died out completely. A relative calm had been restored and quiet prevailed for the rest of the night; however, as a precaution, we fired H&I's at selected points around their perimeter until dawn.

The next morning, I was in the gun pit cleaning the tube when First Platoon came back in. They looked like the remnants of a rag-tag army. One of my friends from First Platoon began yelling at me as soon as he was in sight of the gun pit. He was holding up his poncho, showing me the holes in it, and at the same time shouting, "Look at these damn holes! Where the hell were you aiming last night? Those goddamn rounds were landing almost on top of me!"

"I just put them where you guys call them in at. Don't tell me about it. Find out who called it in and complain to him! It was probably that dumb-ass platoon sergeant you guys have." Receiving little or no satisfaction, he continued on toward his hooch mumbling to himself.

Early one afternoon, Hanks came over to the hooch with the mail. Each of us received at least one letter that day, and Oliver even got two small packages. I received four letters: one from Noreen, one from my folks, one from my sister, Kathy, and the other from John's girl friend. Noreen's letters were always perfumed, which drove me crazy. Without hesitation, I always read hers first whenever I received more than one.

My spirits had been soaring high when I finally got around to opening the letter from John's girl friend, but they were soon devastated after reading the first few lines.

> I have not written to you for awhile, because I did not know
> how to tell you that John was killed almost a month ago. It
> has been very hard for me to deal with. I loved him so very
> much. I know how close the two of you were and suspect that
> his death would be hard on you, too. John's family was in-
> formed that he was accidentally shot by another marine,
> while cleaning his .45 automatic pistol. . . .

I felt instant shock and total disbelief. I read the same words
over and over several times before I allowed myself to believe it.
Tears began streaming down my face and I cried uncontrollably.
Throwing the letter down on my bunk, I walked out of the hooch
with my head hung low to hide my tears. Lou apparently read the
letter and followed me outside. He tried to comfort me, saying,
"I'm sorry, man. Is there anything I can do?"

I wouldn't answer him and coldly shrugged off his concern. I
only wanted to be alone. My grief rapidly changed to hatred as I
stood on top of a bunker near the edge of the hill, thinking about
John. With tear-filled eyes, I cried out at the top of my lungs,
"FUCKIN' GOOKS! I HATE YOU ALL, YOU MOTHERFUCK-
ERS!" Lou stood silently alongside the bunker as I continued to
wail. A tremendous amount of anger was pent up inside me, which
needed to be vented off. So much so, that I felt I wanted to avenge
the loss of my best friend on every gook around. I actually wanted
to kill them all, even though they were not the direct cause of his
death.

That night, I got falling-down drunk in an attempt to rid myself of the world of hurt that I was feeling.

4. Fire Truck

On the way back from chow, on Sunday afternoon, Corporal Hanks advised me that they had received orders for me to report to the battalion aid station the next morning. I was to receive some shots that I was due. I had a repugnancy toward needles, but by the same token realized that they were a necessary evil. I also knew, in the back of my mind, that they would get around to me sooner or later. Later would have been much preferred, however.

Resigned to the fact that I had to go, I was determined to hitch a ride on the first transportation out in the morning. That way I might have enough time to get to Da Nang when I finished at battalion. I had not had the opportunity to get to Da Nang since I first arrived in country.

Bright and early the following morning, I waited at the gate with my thumb out as an amtrack came rumbling down. Its driver had his head poked above the hatch, while the gunner sat behind a .30 caliber machine gun fortified with sandbags. The driver locked up the tracks and it came to a sliding stop alongside the bunker. "Where ya headed?" shouted the driver, over the clanging engine noise.

"Three-seven!" I bellowed.

"Well, hop aboard. We're going right by it," shouted the gunner.

I climbed aboard and planted myself on top, directly behind

the gunner.

Sergeant Mailer had warned me as I was leaving, "You be sure and get back here before the roads close tonight or you'll be in a world of hurt! You understand?"

I told him not to worry and assured him that I would be back in time.

As we headed toward the battalion, we rode through several villes. In one, a middle-aged mama-san, wearing the usual garb (straw hat, white top, and black pants), darted out from the side of the road, dropping what appeared to be a square, bronze-colored tin can directly in our path; then she *didied* out of there like a bat out of hell. The amtrack fishtailed as the driver quickly applied the brakes. We were barely able to stop before running it over. Not knowing what it was, the driver wisely chose to avoid the can and drove off the road, tearing up part of a rice paddy. Then, we came back on again, stopping a safe distance away. Not knowing just where the woman had disappeared to, we cautiously approached the tin can on foot. The gunner stood poised—at the ready—with his machine gun trained in the direction of the ville. I stopped some ten meters from the can, while the driver went directly up to it. With a sigh of relief, he indicated that there was no danger. "It's only a fucking can of water!" he shouted. With that, we climbed back aboard and continued on.

When we got near battalion the driver stopped to let me off at the access road leading to the hill. From there, I walked the rest of the way in.

The first thing I did was check in at the FDC and was greeted by Sergeant Stacker. He told me he was rotating soon and was glad to be going back to the World. I wished him luck. "How's things going out at Hill 65?" he asked.

"Not too bad," I said, "but it would be better if we'd get rid of Mailer."

He cracked a little smile and quipped, "Wouldn't we all! He should be rotating in a couple of months, right?"

I shook my head. "Yeah, Sarge, but it's not soon enough!"

He abruptly changed the subject and said, "You're here to get your shots, huh?"

"Yeah, unfortunately!"

"Well, you'd better hightail it over there."

"Aye aye, sir!"

"Take care of yourself!" he called as I left the hooch.

On my way to the aid station I stumbled across a guy I went through ITR with back in Camp Lejuene.

Timmy Hall was a short, thin-faced, nineteen-year-old Tennessean, with a high pitched voice and a stauch southern accent. In stature, he sort of resembled an elf.

He spotted me first and cried, "Hey ya'll! Where ya'll goin'?"

I looked over and there he was. I couldn't believe my eyes. "Hey, Hillbilly! Is that really you?"

That was the nickname I gave him back in ITR.

"Sure enough!"

"What the hell are you doin' here?"

We talked for a short while. He told me he had been transferred from Lima Company and was on his way to India Company out at Hill 65. He was delighted when I told him he would be at the same fire base as I was. "Listen, I'd love to shoot the shit with you some more, but I've got to get over to the aid station for my shots. I'll see you out at the hill, all right?"

"Okay! You get along now. I'll be seeing ya'll out at the hill."

I took a few steps and called back to him. "Hey! When are you going out there?"

"Tomorrow, I think!"

"Okay. See ya there," I shouted.

At the battalion aid station I received two shots for both smallpox and flu. I made sure that my shot card was filled in properly and signed. If one ever lost his card, all the shots would have to be given all over again. It certainly was not a thought I relished. After getting one of those GG shots in the ass (five CCs worth of gamma globulin), one would limp around in pain for an entire day. I had no desire to allow a corpsman the pleasure of sticking me with needles unnecessarily.

It was still early after getting my shots, so I decided to venture to Da Nang and see what the PX was like. Also, while I was there, I figured that I would hit the MACV office and get a money order to send home.

I made my way toward the access road, passing the FDC on the way. When I reached it I was quite lucky to immediately catch a truck going to Da Nang.

As we rode along, I recalled that prior to leaving Hill 65 that morning, several of the guys insisted that if I did go to Da Nang, I should be sure and bring back a case or two of soda. They would have much preferred beer, but it was SOP that the PX would not sell cases of beer to marines under the rank of corporal. I suppose they didn't trust us or something!

Once we arrived in Da Nang, the driver of the six-by made his way through one of the outlaying streets of an area called Dog Patch. I was told that the area was little more than prostitute's heaven. Both Dog Patch and the city of Da Nang proper were off limits to most and were heavily patrolled by military police.

The street we were traveling was bustling with Vietnamese people and flanked by two- and three-story buildings with balconies and shuttered windows that were in a poor state of repair. I thought to myself, at one time these must have been very grand and stately looking buildings. It's unfortunate that the ravages of war have taken their tolls so dearly as they evidently have.

The truck finally pulled up to the PX and I got off. The area was built up and reminded me of a stateside PX. Behind the sprawling PX was a large outdoor theater area with an enormous stage grabbing one's immediate attention. It appeared as though it could easily accommodate several thousand people. (In fact, it did when Bob Hope presented his USO show in December 1968.)

When I passed through the door of the hanger-sized PX, it

was akin to entering another world. It was a frenzied atmosphere, crammed with GI's searching the aisles and examining the wares. Row after row of vast, multi-tiered counters offered everything imaginable from incidental sundries, such as razor blades and mouth wash, to beverages, such as juice, soda, and alcohol, to material items, such as 35mm cameras and reel-to-reel tape decks. Here one could even order a new car for back in the World. I felt like a child in a candy store.

Having spent a considerable amount of time perusing the giant PX and all of its merchandise, I made several small purchases, including the two cases of soda that the guys wanted me to bring back: one case of Pepsi and one case of Royal Crown.

To one of the starched utility lifer types passing by, I inquired as to where the MACV office was located. He promptly directed me to a building a short distance up the road. I found it easily and secured the money order I wanted, for two hundred dollars. I was getting paid $213 a month. That included combat and overseas pay, too. I kept $13 of it and sent the remainder home. I had been saving for a new Chevy Camaro when I got back to the World.

With everything taken care of that I wanted to do, and with little time left, I returned to the PX area to catch a ride back; however, to my dismay, I found that I had missed the last run to the battalion hill.

As I was pondering what my next move would be, I saw a fire truck slow down as it passed by me; then I heard someone call my name. I was astounded to see a fire truck in the first place, but then for someone to call out my name besides, I was completely astonished.

The voice turned out to be that of Jim Reelings, my old buddy from back in staging and weekend liberty with the rental car. He was grasping on to the back of the fire truck with one hand and madly waving to get my attention with the other. When he did, he yelled, "Where ya going, Ski?"

I yelled back, "Three-seven, but I've already missed the

damn admin run back."

Jim leaped off the back of the truck as it veered toward the building. No sooner had his feet touched the ground then did the truck come to a screeching halt. We were both surprised and very glad to see each other. We shook hands in delight. "How the hell are ya?" Jim asked.

"Great," I replied. "How about you?"

"Real good! So, you've missed your ride back, huh? Well, maybe there's something I can do for ya. We're taking this truck back to my hill, and I'm almost certain that there's a truck going out to Three-seven later today. I work with the transportation scheduling officer in the motor pool. If there isn't, I'll get you a ride back. There's always something going out."

"That would be outstanding! So, how've you been? You look great."

"I've got it made, Ski! All I have to do is worry about getting mortared once in a while. Got AC in the hooch and everything else—it's out of sight!"

"Sure! I knew you'd find a fuckin' easy job."

Just then the driver beckoned for Jim to get going. "We've got to go. Come on, get on, Ski!"

I tossed the two cases of soda on the fire truck and held on tight as we sped away. I had such a weird feeling riding on the back of a fire truck in Nam. The driver began to pick up speed, and before I knew it we were traveling like a rocket. I struggled to keep from being jarred loose. Whenever the truck hit the slightest rut, it went airborne and landed with a tremendous jolt. I was rapidly becoming annoyed and Jim found my plight amusing. "What the fuck's so funny? This guy take driving lessons from Mario Andretti or what?" I bantered.

Jim chuckled and scoffingly warned, "Don't let go!"

"No shit!"

When we arrived, I was never so happy to be back on the ground again.

Jim soon located a supply run going out to 3/7 and instructed the driver not to leave without me. It was scheduled to depart around 1800 hours. In the interim, Jim and I reminisced about the good old times and brought each other up to date on our exploits over a couple of ice-cold cans of Budweiser.

When it was time to leave, I thanked Jim for his help, adding, "Don't forget to look me up if you ever get out my way, you hear?"

"You can bet on it!" he said as we shook hands.

I vaulted onto the back of the truck and settled on a pile of C-rat boxes. The truck pulled out and headed south on the road for battalion. It was the same road I had traveled when I first arrived at battalion several months ago. Already it felt like an aeon ago.

As we approached the access road to 3/7, I leaned over the side of the truck and asked the driver to let me off before he turned in. He nodded in compliance and began slowing down. When the truck came to a complete stop, I jumped off, clutching the two cases of soda and waving an all clear sign to the driver. The truck driver then drove up the access road in a cloud of dust.

Two marines were already there at the side of the road, apparently waiting for a ride as well. I asked them how long they had been waiting, and one said, "About twenty minutes, maybe twenty-five. But nothin' has been by yet!"

I glanced at my watch and saw that it was 1827 hours already. I was beginning to have serious doubts that I would make it back before the roads closed. I kept thinking about what Sergeant Mailer had told me before I left that morning.

The three of us were about to give up hope that something would be along, when a jeep came zooming down the access road with one passenger in the front seat. The jeep slid to a halt in a choking cloud of dust. The driver announced that he was going to Hill 65 if we were in need of a ride. I recognized him as the company commander's driver and greeted him as the three of us climbed on. I sat behind the driver with my feet dangling off the side. There wasn't that much room in the back of a jeep and I had two cases of soda to boot.

The driver was in a *boo koo* hurry to get back before the roads closed. None of us wanted to get our ass shot at, especially by our own. This guy usually drove like a maniac, and this was one time that no one seemed to mind.

Suddenly, without warning, we hit a deep rut in the middle of the road. I was catapulted up and was on my way off the side of the jeep when the guy next to me grabbed hold of my rifle belt and yanked me back in again. "Thanks!" I muttered, as my heart was fiercely pounding away.

"Don't mention it!" he laughed.

It was 1900 hours on the button when we reached the top of our hill. I hopped off and thanked him for the ride. Lifting the two cases of soda onto my shoulders, I marched down to the hooch. There was a small cheer when the guys saw that I was back. Even Sergeant Mailer made an appearance and offhandedly remarked, "I was willing to bet you weren't going to make it."

I detected a slight note of disappointment in his voice and patronizingly said, "Ah, come on, Sarge. . . . I told you I'd be back on time, didn't I?"

His tone changed and he sharply spat, "That was cutting it a little bit fuckin' close."

5.

Mountain Operation

The simple mechanics of an 81-mm mortar are when a round is dropped down the tube, the primer strikes the firing pin located at the bottom of the tube, it then ignites, setting off the explosive cartridge inside the fin assembly of the round; that, in turn, ignites the propellant increments located above the fins. The resulting explosion drives the round up and out of the tube. A bore riding safety pin, in the fuse, pops out sideways from the force of the explosion and rides the inside of the tube. The pin is spring loaded, and once the round leaves the tube, it springs completely out, thus arming the round. As a result of the velocity of the round, as it leaves the tube, and the amount of time that the pin takes to spring out, the round is armed after traveling approximately fifteen feet into the air.

On occasion, we would have a hang round or a misfire in the tube. A hang round is a condition where the round does not make it down to the firing pin at the bottom of the tube. A misfire, on the other hand, does make it to the firing pin, but the round does not fire.

Unfortunately, one cannot tell which the condition is when it occurs, unless one takes the chance of having their head blown off by recklessly peering down the muzzle of the tube; however, there are several steps to take when a round does not fire: first is to wait about ten seconds for a delayed igniton; second is to sharply strike the base of the tube with one's foot to jar loose a hang round. If that fails, the tube is detached from the base plate and raised by the gunner, as the A-gunner precariously surrounds the muzzle of the tube with both hands ready to catch the round as it slides out or is dislodged. As a last resort, the tube can be totally removed from the bipod by the A-gunner and the round can be coaxed out by the gentle tapping of the tube on some sandbags. When a round has to be manually removed from the tube, the safety pin has to be replaced in the fuse, all the increments have to be removed and the round has to be secured in a safe location away from the gun pit.

One time, during a daytime fire mission, we had what we suspected to be a hang round. After performing all the usual steps, the round still had not been dislodged. I began to be concerned that the round was permanently stuck in the tube, rendering it useless. I used less than gentle force striking the tube on the sandbags around the gun pit, to no avail. Then I tried striking it on an empty wooden ammo box, but it had the same result. In desperation, I sat on the ammo box, turned the tube upside down so the muzzle was pointing downward and bounced the muzzle on the box between my legs. I had to do this in such a way as to be able to catch the round before it slid all the way down and struck the box; or else, myself, the tube, and the box would have been scattered into the four winds. After several attempts the round was dislodged. I successfully caught it—in the nick of time—and removed it from the tube. Naturally, while I struggled with it, everyone stayed well clear and offered me no assistance.

Most of the guys exclaimed loud shouts of relief when they saw that I had finally dislodged it. Ned simply shook his head and indicated that I must have been a certified lunatic for doing what I did. He walked away saying, "You're fuckin' *boo koo dinky dow!* You know, Ski?"

A large portion of territory across the Song Vu Gia River, approximately one and a half clicks southeast of our hill, was called Arizona. It was mainly jungle, full of trees, bamboo stalks, elephant grass, rice paddies, insects, and was a safe haven for the gooks. We often fired fire missions out there from the hill and watched frequent air strikes drop napalm and HE throughout the area. Several major operations were conducted to route the VC and NVA operating there. Each time, shortly after they were driven out or wiped out, they returned and operated just as strongly.

To me, it seemed to be a waste of men, time, and equipment to take an area and then pull out and leave it wide open for the gooks to move back in at their leisure. This was the general opinion of most of the others, too. Nevertheless, this seemed to be the operational procedures that our officers stringently followed, no matter where. I often wondered if the politicians back home really wanted to win this war, or just improve the U.S. economy—at our expense.

In early June we were preparing to participate in a major operation (Mameluke Thrust), involving the entire Seventh Marine Regiment, in Quang Nam Province. Our specific area of operation was the surrounding mountains around Hill 65. The operational plans included a sweep thorugh Arizona and, upon completion, insertion by chopper into various areas in the mountains where there were suspected NVA strongholds or activity. We were told that our role in the operation would last as long as a month and would include two companies from our battalion: ours and Lima Company.

I assembled together the equipment I needed: pack, ammo board, gas mask pouch, two canteens, several grenades, my .45 automatic, extra magazines, a trauma dressing, a knife, flashlight, E-tool, flak jacket, and helmet. I took the gas mask out of the pouch and replaced it with C-rats and strapped two HE rounds to the ammo board. Then I placed the canteens, flashlight, and pack containing extra socks, poncho, and other items, onto the ammo board. I made sure it was adjusted correctly and that it felt as comfortable as possible on my back. With all that humping we were going to be doing, I knew it would be cumbersome. I was all set, as far as the equipment was concerned—mentally I was never ready.

Later that night, most of us went to chow and savored the evening meal, knowing full well that C-rats were on the menu for the next thirty days or so.

A good many of us were apprehensive about the operation and, consequently, most managed to get only precious little sleep during the night. As for myself, I had little trouble sleeping, once I finally did fall asleep. It was getting to sleep in the first place that was the problem. It was daybreak by the time I dozed off, and the last thought I remember having was about Noreen's letter.

A few days before, I received the type of letter that any of us dreaded getting—a "Dear John" letter. Noreen let me down very easily. She said that it wasn't because she had found someone new, but because she had made up her mind to enlist in the navy and pursue a career in nursing.

Her letter had a drastic effect on me and plunged my spirits to the lowest level I had yet known. To me, anyway, knowing that my girl was there waiting for me when I got back to the World was a source of strength. It was something to look forward to and a reason to make it back in one piece. It pulled me through some difficult times, and now it would be no more. It left a deep void; she was very special, and I was extremely fond of her.

That night I made a strong effort to douse my feelings of hurt and despair with a bottle of gook rum; however, I merely succeeded in making myself physically sick, which only added to my misery.

Both Ken and Lou were sensitive to my need for understanding and support. They were there when I needed a sympathetic shoulder to cry on and knew just what to say to help ease things a little. It seemed as though we each took a turn fulfilling that roll for one another at some point during our thirteen months.

Morning came quickly and the order to saddle up came with

it. I knew I had to get Noreen off my mind or suffer the consequences. I needed to keep my wits about me. Being careless while out in the boonies could have a deadly effect.

We were all set to go and had already pulled up both guns and the aiming stakes. The front door and windows of the hooch were secured, because we were leaving some of our gear behind. I made sure that I remembered the cleaning pole and had it rammed down the tube with the end sticking out. Vic placed the gun sight into the sight box and carried it as his part of the gun.

When we all assembled on the road in front of the hooch, Sergeant Mailer made a hasty, last minute inspection of all the gear. He acted somewhat jittery, as though he anticipated having a problem. The thought crossed my mind, How might Sergeant Mailer fair out *this* operation? However, it quickly vanished and I directed my thoughts to the concerns at hand.

Each of the four ammo humpers carried three rounds in addition to their part of the gun. We packed a majority of HE rounds, followed by illumination and only a few WP. The other gun squad did likewise. The grunts took along four extra boxes, giving us an additional supply; however, that small amount would not last us very long without being resupplied.

The company moved off the hill, passed through several small friendly villes, and made its way out to the Song Vu Gia River. The river was higher than usual, due to the last few days of heavy rain. The rain marked the beginning of the fast approaching monsoon season. We took a short break before crossing the river and then quickly moved over the sandy bank and into the wood line.

The day grew hotter and the weight of the tube and my equipment became agonizingly heavier by the step. Each of us carefully moved through the jungle, constantly on the alert for an ambush or booby traps; an unseen tripwire was an ever-present fear. The gooks were deviously proficient at converting dud mortar rounds or bomb shells into deadly devices for the unwary. One wrong step could maim or snuff out a life in an instant—your own, your buddy's, or anyone's near you. We moved steadily along on the previously existing trails, although sometimes we had to cut our own, and swept a good portion of Arizona before dark.

At dusk, the word was passed along for us to set up our guns, but not to seat the base plates unless we had to. The CO didn't want to unnecessarily advertise our position. Several ambush patrols were sent out from each platoon and several LPs were set up around the perimeter for additional security.

I sat off to one side of the gun while Vic and Lou sat opposite me on the ground. We quietly ate our C-rats cold and settled in for the first night out. The insects were just as hungry as I was and their attack was relentless. I was forced to roll down my shirt sleeves and button up my collar to expose as little flesh as possible. Even so, the mosquitos had a field day.

Once I began to relax a little, I became cognizant of my fiercely aching feet. When I removed my boots it was like pulling my feet from an oven. My socks were soaked from perspiration and clung to my feet as I peeled them off one at a time. Even though the air was warm, it felt cool circulating around the damp skin. A quick examination revealed two rather large blisters, one on each heel. I drained them, taped them up, put on a dry pair of socks, and carefully inserted my feet back into my boots; then, I placed the wet socks inside my shirt to dry from my body heat. Finally, I curled up on the ground and covered myself with my poncho.

As tired as I was, sleep eluded me. A shower of thoughts raced nonstop through my mind, and reflections of Noreen captivated most of them.

Suddenly, a loud explosion off to the left of our position shattered my thoughts. A rush of anxiety plowed through me like a bulldozer. I felt myself trembling inside and out. Immediately after, a volley of loud whispers flew back and forth as buddies checked on one another. Then, a second later, there was utter silence. Not knowing where or when the next round might hit preyed on my mind for hours, until I must have passed out from sheer exhaustion.

Our lines were probed only once that night and there was no further contact.

By first light the ambush patrols were back in. One of the LP's reported the movement of a small patrol; however, they had moved through the area, apparently unaware of our presence.

With the day's course of action planned, we were on the move again. A couple of hours out, Third Platoon made contact and a brief fire fight ensued. They had stumbled upon a small cache of rice guarded by several poorly armed gooks. When it was over, the captain was delighted. He had his first body count of the operation. He ordered the rice burned and we pushed on.

Later in the day, our company was ambushed. Before an air strike was called in, we had exhausted half of our ammo supply for the gun. A Medivac was called in also and our one KIA and seven wounded were choppered out. The body count increased to sixteen confirmed.

That night, we were probed several times at different locations around our perimeters. For me, it was an instant flashback of the previous night. Everyone was kept on their toes and we scarcely managed much sleep for the second night in a row.

The CO called in for a resupply for the next morning. He chose a clearing about an hour's hump away. Once there, we secured a perimeter around the LZ and awaited the arrival of the choppers.

The company's RO made contact with the incoming choppers and informed them that we would pop a smoke marking the LZ. The CO gave the word and a smoke grenade was tossed into the clearing. A minute later a voice came over the radio: "We roger your yellow smoke, India One."

The LZ was large enough for both UH-34 choppers to put down at the same time. A Cobra gunship circled overhead while they landed. Once they touched down the supplies were hastily off-loaded and the choppers were off the ground again without incident. As they cleared the LZ, some small arms fire could be heard in the distance. I suspected from the sound that it was probably a couple of VC firing at the choppers in vain. Seconds later, the gunship swung around and opened up with their minigun, putting an abrupt end to the harassment.

We had been resupplied with the necessities: ammo, C-rats, and water. Once the supplies were distributed, we immediately pushed on again.

Sometime later, we came to an open stretch of rice paddy about three hundred meters wide. When First Platoon began to cross the dikes, automatic weapons fire opened up from the wood line across the paddies.

Instantly my heart beat increased tenfold. I could almost feel the adrenalin as it rocketed through my veins like an express train.

A second later a hail of machine gun fire sliced through our position, ripping up everything it hit. Pieces of vegetation mixed with splinters of wood flew everywhere. The first few seconds were totally chaotic. I didn't have time to think; my body just reacted. I dove for the nearest cover and landed on the tube I was carrying. When I went to roll over, I felt an excruciating pain centered in my right hip, as a milky white flash impaired my vision for a fraction of an instant. The first thought to cross my mind was that I was hit, but to my relief I discovered that I had severely bruised my pelvic bone instead. Nonetheless, it was agonizingly painful.

Second Squad was able to make it back to cover, but First Squad wasn't as fortunate. They were still in the open and pinned down in the muddy, leach-infested water of the rice paddy with two wounded.

Finally, a barrage of return fire was directed into the wood line as we threw up the gun. The pain in my hip was overridden by the demand from my brain to function. I had to wrestle with my ammo board in order to shed it from my back. Once free, I stood and dropped one round of illumination to set the base plate. Then we were able to fire at the wood line by direct lay. This was done by simply pointing the tube at the target and estimating the distance, elevation, and charge, and then firing away.

In the meantime, Third Platoon circled around to their flank, moved in, and were able to effectively assault and overrun the gooks' position.

After forty minutes of fierce fighting, it was over. A heavy odor of cordite hung thick in the air. By that time the pain in my hip returned, but was much less severe. I was fortunate that it wasn't fractured.

During the attack, we had suffered three KIAs and fifteen others wounded, including Oliver. He was grazed in the leg by shrapnel from one of two RPGs that landed very near to the gun while we were firing. The way hot shrapnel was whizzing through the air, it was miraculous that more of our gun squad wasn't hit. Oliver was medivac'd out with the other wounded, and as a result he sat out the rest of the operation.

The body count had risen to thirty-nine confirmed, and our booty consisted of one rice cache and an array of weapons: from detonation cord to AKs, to a 60-mm mortar. We spent one last night in Arizona without incident and were told we should be prepared to be choppered out the next morning. We were heading for the mountains southwest of Hill 65—precisely, Hill 1242.

When morning came, everyone moved into position around the perimeter of the LZ. Within a few minutes, we heard several choppers approaching and readied our gear for boarding. The CH-46s landed two at a time in a good-sized clearing. Once on the ground, we fought the wash of its rotor blades as we rushed out in groups of six. The dust storm that they created was nearly blinding. Anything loose violently flew around in the turbulence. Crouching down as we approached, we swiftly boarded by way of the rear entrance ramp. The crew chief stood in the opening and rapidly motioned us on board.

Within a matter of seconds we were airborne. Sharply banking to the right, the chopper shuttered briefly as it gained altitude. The cool rush of air was welcomely refreshing, but it only momentarily distracted the trepidation I felt inside. Minutes passed like seconds, and sooner than I had expected we were descending. The combination of engine noise, the rotor blades cutting through the air, the resulting vibrations, and the sound of the wind whipping by, made it virtually impossible to carry on an audible conversation with the person sitting next to you, so we sat there staring blankly into thin air and wrestled with our own thoughts.

We were cautioned about a possible hot LZ and went in prepared to land under fire. First Platoon and our gun squad were the first to be inserted into the LZ. When we arrived, we were met with no resistance at all. Once on the ground, two squads from First Platoon and our gun squad were assigned to secure the perimeter of the LZ.

The entire mountain looked like it had been prep-fired before we landed. Very few trees remained standing, and those that did looked like props for a horror film, with only a few scraggly branches remaining near the tops. Splintered tree stumps and broken limbs protruded from the earth everywhere. In an instant, a chill raced up my spine, leaving me with a strange and eerie feeling about the mountain.

We cautiously moved out of the small clearing at the top and soon found a suitable location for our gun pit in another small clearing about one hundred meters down from the LZ.

Once the gun was set in, we put together an ammo bunker from several of the empty ammo boxes and then dug ourselves in. Lou and I agreed to share a foxhole directly below the gun pit. There had been a good-sized hole there to begin with, and a minimal amount of digging made it big enough for the two of us. We sheltered the top from the daily downpour, which kept everything damp and only added to the gloom of the already dreary mountain top.

The sky seemed to open up every afternoon without fail, causing the gun pit to fill with water and overflow into our foxhole. It took several days before we were able to patch all the leaks and divert the water away from us.

The nights were cold and compelled us to wear field jackets to keep warm; however, they were quickly shed as the sun rose and the heat of the day pressed on. Insects presented almost as much of a problem as the gooks did. I was endlessly applying bug juice to all the exposed portions of my body. Despite the effort, I received dozens of bites anyway.

The third morning on the mountain brought with it the first of several resupply choppers. They replenished our dwindling supply of ammo and provided a welcome diversion from C-rats. For the first time, we were supplied with some new long-rats; new to us anyway. They were dehydrated meals sealed in waterproof packets. To prepare them, water was simply added to the ingredients in the plastic pouch and then mixed together. They were simple to prepare, rather good tasting, and satisfying.

Red Cross packages were also handed out. Each contained soap, writing paper, cigarettes, and a few other miscellaneous items. They were designed to be morale builders and were effective, for those seemingly insignificant items were a luxury to us out in the boonies.

Up to this point, smoking cigarettes had not been one of my vices. I had always given my share of cigarettes away to those that smoked; however, under the circumstances, I stopped giving them away and started smoking myself.

For eleven days we humped from place to place, up and down the mountains. We rarely stayed in one spot for more than a day or so. During that time, we had little contact with the elusive enemy. It was obvious they were there, for signs of their presence were detected many times. Several of their camps were discovered where hasty retreats were made—sometimes only minutes before our arrival; however, it was just as obvious that they chose to avoid contact with us. We were the superior force and they knew it. Subsequently, they chose to wear us down by attrition. Their booby traps were responsible for fourteen casualties—five dead and nine wounded.

A week later, the battalion CO decided to cut the operation short and ordered us to wrap it up within two days. It was none too soon, for we were all weary, almost to the point of exhaustion. We were becoming careless and our nerves were starting to fray at the ends. When we were not humping through the mountains, we were at one another's throats. A couple of serious squabbles broke out. At one point Ned and Lou were ready to throw hands over something really asinine. Ned had lost his C-rat opener and wanted to borrow Lou's. When he reached over to take it, he accidentally lost his balance, fell into Lou and spilled Lou's can of crackers. Vic had to jump in and break it up before it escalated too far. All of that humping and no contact was extremely frustrating for all of us.

The eighteenth day officially concluded the operation. The following morning, our company was ferried back by chopper to Hill 65, and Lima Company to battalion.

Once back, I equated my feeling of being back with that of returning home. The sense of security derived from the familiar surroundings was most comforting; however, we were all still in a daze from the arduous ordeal of trying to kill the enemy and survive ourselves while humping the boonies for two and half weeks straight. For me to have taken part in an operation that searched out and destroyed the enemy was strangely gratifying, almost exhilarating, yet frightening. This operation combined with my first several months in country had a very definite impact on me— it had altered my naiveté forever.

A delightfully unexpected show of Puff in action greeted us on our first night back on the hill. Puff—short for Puff the Magic Dragon—was an AC-47 transport plane, outfitted with three fixed miniguns and huge illumination flares. Puff would wander the skies in search of targets to rain a curtain of bullets upon. Its guns emitted an unmistakably identifiable sound like a distant ship's horn resounding in the fog. It was a formidable weapon that was certainly dreaded by the NVA.

In an odd sort of way, watching Puff work an area was like attending a ballet—it performed so gracefully—with the air between the ground and sky as its stage. To truly appreciate its unnatural beauty, it had to be viewed from afar. The plane would arc the blackened sky, pop a flare and then commence firing on its target. Every fifth round was a red tracer and all that could be seen was a continuous, unbroken, and erratic line of red, emanating from what appeared to be out of nowhere, for Puff always flew its missions without navigational lights. Occasionally, an enemy's single green tracer could be seen shooting upward, vainly seeking out the elusive dragon in the sky.

6. Phu Loc-Six

Six days after we returned to Hill 65, the Fourth of July was exuberantly celebrated by every U.S. military–held position in I Corps. It was one of the few holidays that held any special significance. Everyone took time out from what he was doing, and any non-essential duties or patrols were dispensed with for the day. We were Americans fighting a war in a far-off land, but we still took the time to recognize and to celebrate the Independence Day of our country.

Two days before, Harvey and I had the foresight to plan ahead and purchase an adequate supply of liquor. We procured two bottles of rum, a bottle of Forty-Five, and a bottle of Canadian Club from our local ville. Needless to say, Harvey had to take advantage of the seldom afforded opportunity to call upon the skivvy house while we were there. Against my better judgment, he coaxed me into the hooch by appealing to my humanity rather than to my intelligence. I had some serious reservations about the wisdom of his foray and strongly expressed my apprehensions about our safety, for I knew he would hardly be in a position to respond instantly. Nevertheless, Harvey tactfully skirted my concerns and disappeared into the adjoining room, leaving me with only his weapon and the worry of our security.

We were the sole marines among all the villagers. I had no idea of who, if any, was a VC or VC sympathizer. I felt extremely uncomfortable with an old papa-san and mama-san squatting on straw mats in the corner of the room. From the instant we entered the hooch, neither one moved nor uttered a word. I positioned myself in the shadows of the doorway, crouched on the dirt floor, with Harvey's M-16 at the ready. My nerves were tense as I glanced from outside to the old couple in the corner to back outside again. The entire time, I was watchful for the slightest sign of unusual behavior that would indicate trouble in the ville. Too many careless men had been destined for body bags, and I had no intention of increasing the statistics.

Having waited for what seemed like an eternity, Harvey finally emerged from the back room, buttoning up his trousers and gleaming with contentment. Behind him tiptoed a young girl—she could hardly have been more than sixteen years old—with milky white skin and waist-length hair, who coquettishly inquired if I was next. Tersely indicating that I wasn't, we made a hasty departure. It wasn't until we reached the worn footpath leading to the top of the hill that I was able to relax my guard.

What better way to properly celebrate the Fourth than to break out the booze. We began to party in earnest in the late afternoon and our merriment continued into the night. As soon as it became dark, every hill, as far as the eye could see, was popping hand flares, star clusters, and shooting up illumination rounds. Streamers of red, green, and white exploded above each hill, simulating our own fireworks display. Some were even entwined with tracer rounds arcing high into the night. To an onlooker, it was an impressive sight that went on for hours. It became an impromptu contest among the surrounding hills, each trying to outdo the next. It seemed as though everyone got caught up in the excitement. It was spontaneous and enthralling—like a fire fight. The gooks must have thought that we were all *boo koo dinky dow,* or maybe tripping out on dope.

The first month I was in country (on the battalion hill), several of us had to select three choices from a list of R&R locations.

There were many and some as far away as Hawaii and Australia. They varied in the amount of days, from five to seven, depending on their distance.

I had picked Japan as my first choice and Hong Kong and Bangkok as the second and third respectively. Choosing R&R was based on seniority and each unit was allowed a certain quota. There were just so many available slots open for each location. I had decided on Japan because some relatives of mine were living there at the time.

I wrote home and asked for their address so I could write to them about the possibility of my staying there while on R&R; however, my mom's letter informed me that they had recently moved back to the States. Well, "The best layed plans of mice and men . . . " I concluded it was for the best anyway, for I was saving for the Camaro and the money would be better spent on the car.

Up to this point none of the guys I had arrived with in country had gone on R&R, but most were eagerly awaiting their turn. Usually, one's turn came once one had about six to seven months in country. We were only nearing our fifth.

Vic had just returned from his R&R in Singapore and had everyone drooling and hanging on each word as he described in vivid detail how this outstanding looking chick gyrated all over his body for five whole days. Hoots and howls echoed off the walls of the hooch, as each guy pictured himself in Vic's place.

Hanks and Al Butler had returned from evening chow and were eager to tell everyone the scuttlebutt that was circulating the chow hall. The word was that the company's gunny, Sergeant Webster, found a message scribbled on his shower wall written in red paint. It was alleged to have read "Webster, you chicken shit! The next operation you ain't coming back alive!"

We were all stunned with surprise that someone had written it; however, it probably expressed the sentiments of most of us very well. There were very few that Sergeant Webster hadn't pissed off in the company. He was the type that could have easily pissed off the Pope, given half a chance.

I wondered out loud what Captain Drew was going to do about it, if anything. Vic interrupted, "He'll probably conduct an investigation and someone will get office hours or even court-martialed."

"Maybe not. I understand that the CO thinks he's an asshole too," chimed Lou.

"Well, whatever happens, Webster better lay low or someone just might blow his ass away before the next operation comes around," Ned interjected.

"Fuck it! Who cares—it's not our ass. He deserves whatever the hell he gets, as far as I'm concerned," I retorted.

"Yeah, fuck him! I wonder how he likes it now? He always plays head games with everybody else," added Ken.

For the next few days the gunny disappeared from sight and just about everyone from our company walked around with a big grin on his face. As Lou always liked to say, "I suppose the asshole got the message."

Card playing was a major pastime for most of us. We spent hours huddled around a wooden ammo box table, covered with a drab green blanket, dealing cards by candlelight and playing into the wee hours of the morning.

Poker and blackjack were usually played for money, and back alley, canasta, scrimmage, and double solitaire were mostly played for fun, with no stakes. Gambling wasn't permitted, but it was one of those things that was tolerated and mostly overlooked.

Several of the guys played religiously each payday. As a result, they were broke for the rest of the month.

I never had the need or the desire to gamble like some of the guys did. Oliver was like me and rarely did either. Harvey, on the other hand, was an excellent gambler and regularly sent home hundreds of dollars each month. At the opposite extreme was Brunnell; he always played until he lost every cent he had and then went into debt. He never learned that he wasn't a winner.

I first learned how to play back alley by watching the others play. It seemed to be confusing at first, but I readily became a very good player. The game was similar to another card game called hearts. We played so much that Ken and I became permanent partners and would take on any challengers. We devised very subtle signals to let each other know what we were holding, or the suit we may have been out of, or when to go out. It worked extremely well and we rarely lost a game. Everyone else had signals too, but ours apparently were more efficient.

During the last week of July, I was unfortunate enough to pull mess duty for five days. This time, it had its advantages, though; I got to eat whatever I liked and was allowed to take back a few extra things to the hooch at night. While on mess duty, I had to be up very early in the morning to start things going before morning chow. By the same token, at night I could sleep through, even though my gun squad had gun duty.

In our hooch, we had a PRC-88 field phone that would ring when there was a fire mission. In time, we all became accustomed to waking up instantly to its ring. We were like Pavlov's dogs; we were conditioned to react.

One night, after working all day at the chow hall, I was exhausted. I told Oliver, who had radio watch when I had to get up the next morning, to be sure and wake me up on time; then I was out like a light as soon as I hit my rack.

The next morning at the chow hall everyone was talking about how we got hit the night before. I thought they were busting my balls, because I knew nothing about it. They insisted that it happened and I just wouldn't believe them.

Later that night when I got back to our area, I asked Lou and Ned about it. They confirmed that we had indeed been hit and that they had fired for over an hour on our gun.

Finally, I was convinced that it really did happen and I went nuts. I was so perturbed that no one woke me, that I snarled at everyone in the hooch, "I can't believe I slept through the gun firing! You mean to tell me that we got hit and no one woke me? Why the hell didn't someone get me up? The fuckin' hooch could've got hit. . . . I could've got blown away! I can't believe you guys left me in here that whole time! Please, the next fuckin' time, get me up, will ya?"

"Hey, Ski . . . we're sorry! We only thought you'd rather get some sleep than be jerking around on the gun," said Ned apologetically.

"Well, fuck that man! Next time get me up!" I snapped, still unappeased. Then, I stormed out of the hooch to clear my head.

Later that evening, Sergeant Mailer called both squads together and passed on the orders that he had received earlier that day from battalion. He told us that one of our gun squads had to go to Phu Loc-Six and take over the area while the gun squad that was stationed there went out on an operation with Mike Company. He chose our gun squad to go, along with Corporal Hanks and the new RO. The other gun squad would remain on Hill 65 with him.

Slack had rotated a few weeks earlier and his replacement was just new in country. The new RO was Steve Lybin. He was from Staten Island, New York. He was a stout eighteen-year-old with fair skin, somewhat of a scatter brain, but likable. He fit right in with the rest of us with no problem.

Later that afternoon, most of us were in the gun pit getting some things together for the move, when I noticed two choppers coming out of the valley. They were flying pretty low. As they got closer I could make out that one was a UH-34 followed closely by a Huey gunship. The '34 was leading the way north past the west side of the hill, when for no apparent reason the Huey started to spin out of control and just dropped straight down, crashing into the ground. They went down in a clearing, about three hundred meters out, midway between our hill and a small ville. The skids collapsed upon impact, the rear boom snapped in two, and the props broke like match sticks. Luckily, the impact didn't rupture the fuel tank and explode. Even so, I didn't think anyone survived the crash.

For an instant, I couldn't believe my eyes. When I realized what had happened, I yelled for the others to look. Ned immediately threw the gun in that general direction, anticipating that they may need some fire support.

The pilot of the usually lethargic UH-34 swung the chopper around and landed it nearby within a matter of seconds. I never saw one move so fast. I was impressed. As he was landing, I could see several figures crawling from the wreckage. They quickly moved away from the chopper and then dropped to the ground. My guess was that they thought it still might explode and wanted to be well clear if it did. The crew of the UH-34 picked up the survivors in a matter of a minute and *didied* out of there posthaste.

After the rescue, each of us speculated on what caused the chopper to go down. I thought that it must have had some type of engine malfunction. But Lou insisted, "I know why! Some goddamned gook was dinging away and got lucky and hit it. Probably hit a hydraulic line or something and they lost pressure. That's why it dropped like it did."

No one else dared to venture their opinion after Lou's seemingly learned oratory.

Not one of us had ever been at Phu Loc-Six, except for the times when Oliver and I used to walk the morning road sweeps from battalion. We never went in, though; we only went to the main gate and then returned to battalion again. All I knew about it was that it was flat, sandy, and right on the river.

The next day battalion sent over a six-by to transport us to Phu Loc-Six. We loaded up the gun, all of our gear, and then climbed aboard. Lou and I stood behind the cab, leaning on the roof while the others sat on the benches. Sergeant Mailer had a few departing words of wisdom as we pulled away: "You guys stay the hell out of trouble and have a nice vacation while you're out there."

Once we were out of earshot, Lou declared, "What an asshole

that guy is," as he shook his head in disbelief.

We drove away from the hill and back toward battalion, then we cut off onto another road heading toward Phu Loc-Six. It was the same road that we used to sweep each day. There were several small villes that dotted the road along the way. As we approached Phu Loc-Six, the rice paddies took over where the villes ended.

As we passed by, I could see several old mama-sans, garbed in black silk pants, white tops buttoned all the way to the neck, and straw hats, bending over as they worked in the rice paddies. There was one little baby-san, about eight or nine years old, leading a rather large water buffalo by the nose. He was pulling it with a rope and hitting it on the head with a long stick to make it move. The water buffalo seemed amazingly content to allow itself to be prodded by the child, even though it could have easily resisted.

We arrived at our destination and found our way to the gun pit. Everywhere one looked there was sand. Even the gun pit was a large circle dug into the sand. It was about two feet below ground level and was shored up by wooden slats driven into the ground. All three ammo bunkers were outside the gun pit just a few feet away. The FDC hooch was right next to the gun pit and our hooch was behind that.

We were situated almost on the bank of the Song Thu Bon River. From one side of the gun pit area, we could look out over the river. There was a small embankment a few feet away, then a short drop to the water's edge. Off to the left was a fairly large wooden bridge constructed in a latticework fashion, which ran from one side of the river to the other. At the far end of the bridge was a look-out tower. Beyond that was a large span of flat grassy area before the wood line began. A mountain range loomed up in the far distance and was shrouded in a bluish haze. On the opposite side of the gun pit was a narrow sandy road that wound its way through the compound. There were numerous hooches of various sizes and shapes, and an array of telephone poles scattered throughout. In all, the compound itself wasn't very large. By the same token, we didn't want for space either.

The first few things we did were set the gun in and check out the ammo supply. We were happy to discover that there was a sufficient amount of ammo, especially since we didn't bring any along. There were only a few rounds opened, so we broke out enough just in case we had to fire a prolonged fire mission.

Corporal Hanks and Steve Lybin went to set up in the FDC hooch while the rest of us settled ourselves in our new hooch. The hooch had a wooden floor, with wooden sides about four feet high with screening above that, a metal roof, and a screen door on each end. The seven of us felt almost lost in it. We each grabbed a rack and made ourselves at home.

I claimed a rack in the middle of the hooch on one wall, and Al took the rack opposite mine on the other wall. The only place I found to store anything was a couple of narrow shelves built into the wall above my rack, so the rest of my things I placed either on my rack or beneath it.

Once we got everything squared away, Ned and I walked over to the FDC hooch. It was small, but certainly adequate for its purpose. The one-room hooch had three racks in it and the FDC area, which was located in the right hand corner as we entered the door. A slant top desk held the plotting board and the necessary range charts. A PRC-25 radio, a PRC-88 field phone, and a hand phone for the gun pit were located next to it on a small table. A single bare light bulb hung above the desk. There was even a comfortable rattan chair to sit in.

"Not bad . . . not bad at all!" I said to Ned, looking around as we walked in.

"Shit, look at that! Now that's real class," Ned exclaimed.

He was pointing to the real wood paneling in the FDC corner of the hooch. It rose from floor to ceiling and was a light color wood that had some type of clear varnish on it.

"Damn! These guys have all the comforts—wood paneling, a rattan chair, a roomy hooch—all the pleasures of home," I quipped.

"Yeah, no wonder they didn't want to leave this place!" Ned

chuckled as he plopped down in the rattan chair and propped his feet up on the table. "I think I'm going to really like it here," he said, pondering the thought.

Wondering if the phones worked, I motioned with my thumb in their direction and inquired from Hanks, "Did you check 'em yet and do they work okay? It would be a hell of a time to find out they don't work when we need to use 'em."

"No, I didn't. Why don't you go out there and we'll check the gun pit phone first. Then we'll check the phone in your hooch."

"All right. I'll let ya know."

I went to the gun pit and found that it worked fine; then I went over to our hooch and found that the buzzer on the PRC-88 was okay, too. Good thing, because we were the only gun squad, and we would have to fire any and all fire missions that came our way.

Ned moseyed back to the hooch a few minutes later, just as Lou realized that he was getting hungry, so the three of us went in search of the chow hall. To our delight, we found it just across the road from our hooch. That made it most convenient for us to get our food, then walk back and eat in the privacy of our own hooch. It was one of life's little amenities, indigenous to Phu Loc-Six.

The first couple of days were rather quiet. We were only called on once to fire a fire mission. It was kind of strange, but I noticed an absence of officers around. At least in our area. No one came around to hassle us. We were pretty much on our own.

One night, a few days before we left Hill 65, I found a captain's insignia lying on the floor in the tower. No one saw me pick it up, so I put it in my pocket and kept it. It was obvious that Captain Drew must have lost it there. I brought it with me, and since there was no one around except us, I decided to put it on my cover and wore it around our area. The guys got a kick out of it. They played along and were saluting and calling me "the Old Man." After a while I simply forgot that I had it on.

The next day, after lunch, I was taking a nap on my rack when a reactionary platoon came in from the boonies for a stand down.

Some grungy looking gunnery sergeant came in our hooch looking for a few extra racks for his mortar section. He must have seen my cover hanging over my rack with the captain bars on it and said to Ned, "Is he a *captain?* He looks kind of young!"

Ned woke me up as soon as the gunnery sergeant left the hooch. He was excited as he told me about the company coming in. Then, when he mentioned what the gunnery sergeant had said, I went into an immediate panic and nervously asked him what it was that he had told him. Shrugging his shoulders, he said, "I told him you just made captain not too long ago."

"Did he believe you?"

"I don't know. I think so."

"Shit! That's just what I need—to get caught impersonating an officer! Then Mailer would really have my ass in a sling!"

"Ah, don't worry about it," he replied, phlegmatically. "Just take them off and forget about it. Nothing will happen."

I did, and much to my relief nothing ever came of it. I suppose the gunnery sergeant dismissed me as just another young-ass officer. There were an awful lot of young junior officers in Nam.

That evening, we were out back shooting the breeze with the guys from the mortar squad that had arrived earlier. They had set up their gun in the rear of our hooch and were firing a fire mission for one of their patrols on the far side of the river bank.

I found it quite odd that their gunner took the sight off the gun each time they fired. It seemed to be a waste of time and surely shook the gun sight off the aiming stakes when he did. When I mentioned it to him, he informed me that they have always fired that way and he didn't find it a problem. I thought to myself, *Who was I to tell him how to set up his gun?* So, I just dropped the subject.

They only stayed the night and pulled out the next afternoon. I didn't know where they were headed, but I was glad it was them and not us.

Minutes before they left the main gate of the compound, a

tank retriever lumbered in dragging another tank in tow. Rumbling and clanking along, the two tanks passed the departing marines and came to a sudden halt only a stone's throw away from our gun pit. Left behind, in the soft sandy road, was a long trail of distinctly recognizable tread marks.

The tank that was in tow was in pretty bad condition. It looked like it had been in the boonies for some time. Its track was completely gone from the right side, the right fender was bent up like a pretzel, the machine gun turret at the top was damaged and was dangling off to one side, part of the muzzle was missing and what remained of it looked like a peeled banana. To top it off, a good portion of the tank was caked with mud and dried vegetation. It reminded me of the target that we had used when I trained on the 3.5 rocket launcher, back in ITR. It also had been blown to hell.

The scuttlebutt was that the tank was one of several that had been ambushed and left out in the boonies when its engine quit. The reason for the muzzle looking like a peeled banana was that the gooks had booby-trapped it and someone apparently neglected to check the barrel before firing. Consequently, it exploded—killing the crew.

Somehow, that story just didn't wash. No one in his right mind would attempt to fire that gun without first checking it out, especially since it had been out there for a while. The more likely scenario was that it blew up accidentally during the ambush, killing its crew as a result. At any rate, I grabbed my camera and snapped a few photographs of it for my photo album.

It was nearly the end of August and we had been at Phu Loc-Six for two weeks. Several days of rain finally broke the heat. As a consequence, everything became sloppy and musty smelling. However, just as fast as everything was soaked by the rain, everything dried up within a matter of a few hours—once the sun reappeared.

As the days went by, the fire missions increased considerably and we frequently fired across the river in support of several operations being conducted there.

One particular day, a small patrol was pinned down and frantically called in for a fire mission on a heavily armed NVA unit of unknown size. We fired two rounds of WP so they could determine if we were on target. WP were white phosphorus rounds that when exploded emitted a white plume of smoke that could easily be seen from a distance. We were right on target and they requested we fire fifteen rounds for effect. That amount of rounds devastated the NVA's position. As a result, it enabled the patrol to safely pull out.

Firing that many rounds in quick succession, and in less than a minute, turned the midsection of our tube into a rainbow of colors. It became extremely hot and had to be left untouched until the heat dissipated.

The Marine Corps Manual's specified rate of fire for an 81-mm mortar was a maximum of twelve rounds per minute for not more than two minutes and a sustained rate of fire of three rounds per minute. Notwithstanding, these figures were ignored and constantly surpassed in actual combat. We didn't have the luxury of going by the book when our own life or someone else's life was at stake.

Both Vic and I received packages at mail call. His was about twice the size of mine. That didn't matter much; it was what was inside that counted. Mine contained some odds and ends and one scarce and a very sought after commodity—booze. It was a fifth of bourbon whiskey (Old Grand Dad). Vic's package included, among other things, a gourmet snack. There was a loaf of Italian bread—a wee bite stale—and several lengths of pepperoni with only a slight bit of mold growing on it.

"Ski, I think the most obvious and virtuous thing for us to do is to combine our assets and have a little party! What do you think?"

"You know, I think that's an outstanding idea. We surely could do justice to this bottle. You want to invite Hanks over to join us?"

"Hell no! Who the hell wants that asshole over here?"

By the time Vic and I shared his gourmet snacks and my booze with the others in the hooch, we only came away with a smidgen of each. But was it savory! It was those seemingly ordinary amenities that afforded us a brief but welcomed diversion from Marine Corps chow.

After just completing a fire mission, all of us were in the gun pit breaking out ammo when Hanks came running out and informed us that he just received a check fire over the radio. That meant we could not fire until further notice, which could have stemmed from any one of a variety of reasons.

We didn't have long to wait, however, to discover the cause. The sound of chopper blades whopping through the air drew our attention to a UH-34 chopper swiftly coming in to land on the embankment on our side of the river. We concluded it probably had some engine problems, because its crew worked on the engine for some time after it landed.

Approximately two hours later another chopper appeared. This one was a much larger CH-53. It was nicknamed the Work Horse. It circled the bridge, which was only a few meters away. After hovering over the disabled chopper, it winched down a steel cable, which was then hooked to the top of the rotor blade housing by one of the crew members of the CH-34. Its main rotor blades had already been tied back and secured before the '53 arrived. Once the cable was connected, the CH-53 lifted the chopper with very little effort and was off in a matter of seconds. All of us who were watching let out a loud cheer as the disabled chopper was lifted up and flown off. Of course I had to get a few snap shots of the action for my photo album.

In a previous package from home, I received a camera that I had asked for in one of my earlier letters. It was a compact camera with automatic winding, a view finder indicator, which indicated if there was enough light or not, and it used 126 cartridge film. It was all very convenient and simple to operate. I took it along most everywhere I went, as long as I had film for it. I would send home the exposed film to be developed and my folks would send back the pictures. That way, they had the opportunity to view the pictures and I got to keep them.

One of our various mundane chores included the disposal of the unused and discarded increments from the rounds that we fired. Each round of HE and WP had nine cloth increment bags containing composition B explosives, while the illumination rounds had four increments of compressed TNT explosive in the form of several thin yellow wafers sealed in plastic wrappers. Some of the increments had to be removed before firing, depending on the distance the round had to travel. It was these increments that were later disposed of by burning. We stuffed them into an empty plastic canister, which was inserted upright in the ground a safe distance from the gun pit and then lit them with a match. We would then stand well clear and watch the resulting flames burst into the air. The combination of the plastic canister and the flames shooting out created a continuous, low-pitched wailing sound. It burned extremely hot and rapidly extinguished itself.

Just after breakfast, Steve came over to our hooch with some good news. He burst in the back door smiling from ear to ear. "Hey, everybody, listen up! We're going back to Hill 65 tomorrow! Hanks just got the word from battalion," he bellowed.

We all perked up in unison. "Shit—all righhht!" Lou gleefully exclaimed.

This place had become a little boring, and I for one was ready to go back. "Outstanding! It's none to soon for me," I shrieked.

Vic looked over at Steve and asked, "Any word on the other gun squad?"

"Yeah . . . Hanks said they're supposed to be back either later on today or the first thing in the morning, right after the road sweep."

"Good! They can have back their sandy hole in the ground they call a gun pit," said Vic sarcastically.

Ned didn't care much, nor did it seem to phase him one way or the other whether he stayed at Phu Loc-Six or returned to Hill 65. He was getting short and had only thirty-six days left before he rotated back to the World.

"Hey, Ned, you don't look very happy! How come?" inquired Brunnell.

"When you get as short as I am, you'll know why," Ned snarled.

I glanced up at Brunnell and then over to Ned. Ned sounded very defensive for some reason and Brunnell was a bit taken back by his rebuke.

Before anyone else could say anything, Ned must have realized the way he sounded and with a note of sincerity in his voice he turned to Brunnell and muttered, "Sorry I jumped in your shit, man."

Brunnell acknowledged his apology with a slight nod. I looked at Ned and asked, "You okay?"

"Yeah," Ned said tersely. "I'm fine."

With that, Hanks walked in the hooch. "Who's minding the store?" I asked.

"Lybin! He just came back."

"Oh! I didn't see him leave."

"So is everybody happy we're going back? I sure am! Fourteen days from today and I sky out of here on a big freedom bird, man! When we get back to the hill, I'll have just enough time left to get my gear together, get my flight date, and do some serious partying."

"Hey, freedom bird, how are we going back tomorrow? . . . by six-by?" Vic asked.

"Yeah, battalion's sending one out for us."

Lou was more than eager to leave and started packing his things together right then. The rest of us waited until later that night.

As dusk was setting in, I caught a glimpse of Ned heading down toward the river bank. Even though he said he was fine earlier, I wasn't convinced, so I tagged along. I found him sitting in the sand, staring at the water. I walked over and sat down beside him. "How's it going, Ned?"

He let out a big sigh and quietly answered, "I don't really know, Ski."

"You're leaving soon, aren't ya, and you've got your girl waiting for ya at home, right?"

"Yeah, but that's part of the problem."

"What do you mean?"

"Well . . . I'm undecided about re-upping for another tour . . . apprehensive about going home if I don't . . . what I'm going to do with my thirty days leave if I do re-up, and I have mixed emotions about leaving all my friends here, no matter what I do."

"What do you mean you're apprehensive about going home?" I retorted.

"I'm not really sure I'll be able to make the adjustment back in the World."

"That's bullshit, man! Of course you'll be able to adjust. You're just out of touch a little with reality. . . . This fuckin' place does it to everybody. It fucks up your head!"

"I—I—just don't know, Ski," he replied, trying desperately to force back the tears.

I put my arm around his shoulder and said, "Now listen to me good. You don't want to re-up in this goddamn place. You've done your time; why press your luck? Go home, get the hell out of the Corps and enjoy yourself! You owe it to yourself; you deserve it!" I said forcefully, but trying to be reassuring at the same time.

He didn't respond, but just sat there for what seemed to be an eternity, attempting, without much success, to stem the tears from swelling up in his eyes. I didn't know what else to say to him, and the prolonged silence left me feeling awkward.

"Ned? . . . "

"I'm fine, Ski. Really, I'll be all right. I just need some time to get my shit together."

After removing his glasses, wiping the tears away and letting out another big sigh, he regained his composure. I stood up, extending my hand and said, "Come on, let's go back to the hooch and pack up our shit."

"Okay," he said, grasping my hand to steady himself as he got up. "Thanks, Ski."

"For what?"

"For caring, I guess," he muttered with a wisp of a smile.

"Sure."

As we walked back, I wondered to myself why Ned seemed to be on the brink of losing it all of a sudden. Up to now, he had always appeared to be in control.

The sometimes overwhelming stress of constant fear, loneliness, killing, the sickening sight of death, the abrupt changes from inactivity one minute to the extremely intense pressure of a sudden fire fight the next, trying to drop rounds in on the enemy before he ranges in on you, and desperately wanting to survive, has a terribly drastic effect on one's mental well-being. Consequently, the pressures are enormous and sadly devastating for some, but clearly manageable for most. Occasionally, some of us teeter on that fine line between rationality and delusion—a few cross over.

The next morning, shortly after the road sweep was completed, a six-by rumbled into the compound transporting a squad of footsore and battered looking marines. They were the rightful tenants of this sandy gun pit and we cheerfully greeted them as they arrived. Wearily, they carted their gear off the truck as we eagerly piled ours on. This same truck would be transporting us back to Hill 65.

Once the six-by was loaded with all of our gear, we made the formal change of command. Hanks checked off the radio net and they checked on.

Vic made one last check of the gun pit and hooch for any

equipment belonging to us that we may have overlooked. Finding nothing, he signaled a thumbs up to Hanks and climbed aboard. We waved farewell as we departed and the truck slowly ambled toward the main gate along the rut-filled sandy road.

7.   Reconstruction

The trek back on the beat up old six-by was quite uneventful. That particular truck surely had seen its better days, nonetheless, it safely delivered us back to Hill 65—or so we thought. The driver had to negotiate a sharp right turn off the main road and inadvertently ran the right rear tandem wheels into a deep ditch. In order to get free, he made several attempts at rocking the truck back and forth, gunning the engine as he skillfully maneuvered the gears from first to reverse and back again. After being involuntarily volleyed about like a handful of Ping-Pong balls, those of us in the rear of the six-by decided to reduce the load and climbed out. Then, with the load lightened, the driver tried again. This time on its forward thrust, the wheels hesitated for a instant as the weight of the truck teetered on the lip of the ditch and then grudgingly rolled forward. With apparent reluctance, the force of gravity finally succumbed to the truck's rocking motion.

Once liberated, we climbed back aboard and the six-by slowly lumbered toward the guard bunker a short distance up the access road. Everyone aboard cheered when the marine on duty waved us on. As the driver changed gears and accelerated, a large cloud of thick, blue-black exhaust smoke was expelled and hovered behind us like a smoke screen.

I was surprised to see that it was Timmy Hall that was on duty at the bunker. "Hey, Hillbilly!" I shouted over the roar of our six-by's straining engine, waving my arm back and forth to attract his attention.

When he recognized that it was me, he shouted back, "Hey, Ski! How the hell are ya?"

I gave him the thumbs up and yelled back, as we sluggishly proceeded up the hill, "Stop by eighty-ones when you get a chance." He acknowledged by shaking his head, knowing that I wouldn't be able to hear him over all the noise.

As the truck rounded the bend, our area slowly came into view. When we drove over the crest of the hill next to the tower, I looked around and something immediately struck me as appearing strangely odd. For a split second I was puzzled. Suddenly realizing what it was, I nudged Lou and cried, "What the hell did they do? The trenches are gone!"

Lou looked from side to side and replied, "Yeah, they're all covered over! What the hell! . . . "

While we were gone, Captain Drew, in his infinite wisdom, had the engineers bulldoze over the entire trench line on both sides of the hill. Only a few bunkers were left untouched. I saw no logical reason for eliminating the trenches. They only fortified our position. Just the same, they were gone.

We later learned from Sergeant Mailer, that in addition to what was already done, Captain Drew intended for us to tear down all of our hooches, including the FDC hooch, one at a time, then build them below ground.

No sooner had we arrived, when Charlie McDunn (A-gunner for the other gun squad) wanted to hear all about our stay at Phu Loc-Six. Indiana, as most of the guys called him, was somewhat of a prankster and always in a jovial mood. He sported a bucktoothed smile, which complemented his boyish appearance. Furthermore, he blushed at the drop of a hat and, as a result, had perpetual rosy-red cheeks. Charlie, as I chose to call him, was from Gary, Indiana; hence the nickname: Indiana.

"Come on, guys, so tell me about Phu Loc-Six. How was it?"

Before anyone had a chance to answer, he continued, "I heard that—"

"BUZZ—BUZZ"

He was interrupted by the ringing of the PRC-88 field phone, signaling a fire mission. I dashed out of the hooch closely followed by Vic and Lou. Charlie came, too, and stood outside the gun pit ready to lend a hand if needed. Ned was already outside, sitting on the ammo bunker, talking with Al and Ken. "Do we have a fire mission?" Ned asked, as he jumped down into the gun pit.

"Yeah!" I answered and turned to Lou saying, "Break out one WP, just in case we need it!"

During the time Lou was getting out the WP round, Ned kicked the sandbags from the foot of the bipods and I removed the plastic cap from the muzzle of the tube. Vic was sitting on the sandbags, with the phone to his ear, waiting for the FDC to come on. "Are we gonna fire or what?" Ned said impatiently, looking at Vic.

Vic shrugged his shoulders and threw his hands up in the air. "I don't know," he said. "No one's given me anything, yet!"

"What's the matter?" Lou said sarcastically. "Hanks forget how to use the fuckin' plotting board in there?"

Lou's innuendo brought a chuckle from everyone. "All right, everybody . . . forget it. . . . They want us to secure!" Vic said, as he threw the phone down in contempt.

I let out a deep sigh of exasperation and glanced around at Charlie who was still standing there with a whimsical smile on his face. Over his left shoulder, I could see out to where the gun ship had crashed before we left several weeks ago. "Hey! The chopper's gone!" I said.

Charlie swung around to look behind him, then stopped half way when it dawned on him what I was referring to. "Oh, that!" he said. "They took it away with a Skycrane right after you guys left. They came in, collected all the pieces, and away they went."

"Oh yeah! We had a downed thirty-four by us. The only thing

was a fifty-three flew in, hoisted it up, and carried it away, instead."

"How was the chow out there, Ski?"

"Pretty decent. The chow hall was right across the road. We went over and got our chow, took it back to our hooch, and then ate it there," I said matter-of-factly.

"Speaking of chow, I'm getting hungry," said Vic.

"Me too!" cried Al. "How about you, Ski?"

"I'm ready. Let's go!"

That night, after everyone was back from chow and gun drill was over, we sat around the hooch and related our experiences at Phu Loc-Six. I purposely left out the part about the captain's bars, though. When it was Charlie's turn, he told us about the engineers filling in the trenches and all the scuttlebutt that was going around while we were gone, much of which wasn't even worth listening to. What we were most interested in hearing about, however, was the ambitious and seemingly ill-considered project that Captain Drew had concocted. The word was that the other squad's hooch was first on his schedule to be torn down, requiring them to move in with us. That would mean we all would have to readjust to some very cramped quarters in our hooch. No one knew, or they weren't saying anyway, when the CO intended the work to begin. I for one had hoped he would dismiss the notion as being absurd.

Ten days had passed and not a peep was heard about the reconstruction. The old adage, "No news is good news," was holding true. To take its place, some new scuttlebutt was in the air; an army artillery unit was to be stationed at the point. It didn't make much sense to have another artillery battery on the hill, for we had several already. The next day unveiled the mystery.

The army moved in and brought with them two of the biggest guns I had ever seen. They looked like telephone poles on tracks. We were told they were 175-mm. I didn't know we even had anything bigger than 155-mm. The guns were mounted on tracked vehicles, with the driver located in the front left corner. One followed the other, as they cautiously negotiated the road through our area and out to the point. A huge hydraulic plow with large pointed teeth was affixed to the rear and used to brace the gun in its emplacement. A column of various military vehicles motored through behind them, carrying men, equipment, and supplies needed in support. They wasted no time setting in the two guns, laying out their area, and building hooches.

Surprisingly, they made better neighbors than I had expected, though they usually remained within their own area. They were quite self-sufficient and were in want of practically nothing—quite indicative of the army. They moved in everything and anything they needed. They even made regular weekly supply runs to Da Nang with their Armored Personnel Carrier (APC), bringing back pallets of soda and beer.

Whereas we rapidly and frequently exhausted our meager supply of soda and beer, they always had ample supplies of both. The Marine Corps and the army were traditionally at odds with one another, nevertheless, under the circumstances, we actually managed a friendly alliance. It was mostly because we valued their easily accessible and unlimited supply of beer and soda. They, in turn, realized the need for our unqualified support, due to their strategically vulnerable position at the point. It was a coalition that worked well.

Hanks could be heard screaming in the distance, "I'm skying out of here, man! I've got my flight date!" Then, he came rushing into our hooch. "I'm leaving for battalion tomorrow!" he announced excitedly.

"That's terrific, Hanks," Vic acknowledged. "When's your flight date?"

"The eleventh—two days from today!" he cried, glancing around the hooch. He acted like a lost puppy, not knowing where to scamper to next. "Whoopee!" he hollered, as he rushed back out the door in a flash.

"He certainly sounds excited," declared Ned.

"I would be too if I were him and getting the hell out of here!" I pointed out.

A minute later, Lou came through the door dragging his feet. "Guess who got his flight date." I said to Lou.

"Hanks . . . I know. I just saw him doing a Mexican hat dance up the road and he told me," Lou answered, dishearteningly.

"What's the matter?" I asked.

"Nothing. I just get depressed when I see other guys leaving and I'm still here," he sighed as he plopped himself onto his rack.

"Well, I guess we're going to do some partying tonight!" Vic stated.

"Yeah, for him and for us!" Ned was quick to insert.

That night the party plans were spoiled. It hadn't take the gooks long to discover the location of the army's 175s. They apparently decided to test the army's defenses out at the point and probed their perimeter with several RPGs. Even though it was more harassment than anything else (although the army didn't think so) we still had to man the guns throughout the night in case the gooks tried something a little out of character, like attempting a ground attack. Morning slowly crept around, bringing an end to our quiet vigil.

A week after Hanks rotated, his replacement arrived. He was a tall, lanky, dark-skinned black with bulging yellowish eyeballs. He had an unusually high-pitched voice that reached soprano when he became excited. As he liked to put it, he was born in Atlanta, Georgia, and called Philadelphia home.

Sergeant Mailer brought him around after noon chow and made the introductions. When they entered the hooch, he shouted, "All right, everybody, listen up! This is Cpl. Wayne Eastman. He's your new assistant section leader. I expect everybody will get along just fine together."

There was a short pause, then Mailer started with me and made his way, clockwise, around the hooch, naming each of us for Corporal Eastman. In response, Eastman greeted us all together by saying "Howdy, gentleman!" and chuckled with half a smile.

"Where ya from?" inquired Lou.

"Philly. . . . Atlanta, originally," he answered, bobbing his head up and down like he was trying to convince himself. He then directed his attention toward Sergeant Mailer, who was heading out the door, and while still bobbing his head, said, "We ought to get along just fine, Sarge."

Al waited till they were out of earshot and said, "This dude is definitely strange to say the least!"

Vic gave a long whistle as he rolled his eyes in astonishment. I just stared up in the air and muttered, "If first impressions mean anything, bring back Hanks! At least you knew where he was coming from. This guy acts like a zombie!"

Soon after, it became quite evident that Eastman was oblivious to the world around him. Furthermore, he made it crystal clear that he was impervious to reason and lacked the slightest hint of leadership ability. This later led to the build-up of animosity toward him and to some degree was directed back to us as well.

I just stepped out of the hooch for a breath of fresh air when Ned called to me from across the road. He was sitting on top of the bunker. "Hey, Ski? Got a minute? I want to talk to you."

"Yeah, sure. What's up?" I answered, a little puzzled.

Ned hopped off the bunker and we walked down the road a short way. He stopped along the concertina wire and stood looking out over the ville below.

"I just wanted you to know, Ski, that I've finally got my head and ass wired together. I've done a lot of soul-searching and have been trying to sort out what I want to do. Well, I just want you to know that I've decided to get the fuck out of here and not re-up. I'm getting really short, only twenty-one days left to go. I want to see my folks, my girl friend, and my other friends back in the World, too."

"I'm glad you got your shit together. You made the right decision, Ned. You know that, don't you? Before you know it your flight date will be here and you'll be gone."

"Yes, I know. Thanks, Ski. I really appreciated your concern that night out at Phu Loc-Six."

"Ah, forget it, Ned. You would have done the same for me."

Vic had a portable AM-FM radio, powered by four D-size batteries that he had bought at the PX in Da Nang. On Friday nights, several of us gathered around to listen to the oldies that were broadcasted from 2200 hours to midnight. Frequently, Vic and I engrossed ourselves in long and sometimes heated discussions about our favorite songs and radio stations back home, and the memories associated with each of them. Most prominent was WMCA and its disk jockey, Cousin Brucie.

On occasion, Lou would jump in to make it a trio when we harmonized along with just about any acappella tune that was played. We sang a little flat, but who cared?

A very sensual female voice on the radio had been eloquently describing the female vocalist who was about to sing "Harper Valley PTA," as I walked in the hooch. She was Chris Noel, the celebrated female disk jockey of the Armed Forces Radio Network. She had an extraordinarily magnetic personality and undoubtedly was the center of every GI's fantasy. It was beyond dispute; she had the sexiest voice on the air waves.

One day, with no malice intended, she broke the hearts of more than a few when she announced that she would wed a navy officer and then went on to bid us all an emotional farewell. I missed her voice; I felt as though I knew her personally.

Brunnell was in his glory, too, on Friday nights. He was able to stomp his feet and slap his knees to shit-kicking music for an hour prior to the oldies coming on. With no concern to him, he most often listened alone, for none of us were able to tolerate more than a few minutes worth at any one time.

Melody Patterson, of "F-Troop" fame, had usually substituted in the absence of Chris Noel and expectedly took her place when she left. One evening, Vic was listening to the radio when I walked in. "Hey, Ski! Listen to this," he cried. "If you write to Melody, she'll send you an autographed picture of herself."

"Oh, yah! Did you get the address?"

"Fucking-a-right! I jotted it down on this C-rat box top."

Not long after writing to her, in care of the radio station, did I receive two black and white autographed pictures of Melody. One was a provocative pose in a ruffled bikini bathing suit. Wow, did she look outstanding! It was inscribed: "To Ski, lots of love and many kisses, always—Melody Patterson."

At the other end of the radio spectrum was the North Vietnamese version of Tokyo Rose: Hanoi Hannah. If the radio reception was good, we were just barely able to tune in to her broadcast. In a slightly Vietnamese-accented English, her almost melodic, yet singsong voice continuously spewed out manufactured reports, misinformation, and political propaganda. All this, in an effort to undermine her listeners: namely, the U.S. military. She would always manage to have small bits of accurate information on which the remainder of her spiel was based. Often, unit designation and their areas of operation were mentioned. On occasion, she would even have previously unreleased information that she would gloat over and expound upon. Many of us, myself included, found her mere rhetoric entertaining; however, one had to realize that the contents of her program material had the designed intent of being blatantly subversive. With that in mind, we heckled her verbal intercourse and enjoyed ourselves to no end.

It was the beginning of October and all my hoping and finger crossing was for naught. Captain Drew had ordered the construction—or should I say reconstruction—to begin ASAP. To make things worse, Corporal Eastman was placed in charge of the project by Sergeant Mailer. The plan, as far as we were informed, was to relocate everyone into our hooch while we tore down and then reconstructed the other hooch underground.

In the early stages of the project, everything went along smoothly. We spent about three days dismantling the hooch, ammo box by ammo box, and stock piled those that were salvageable. Then, the drudgery of the blister-forming and back-breaking digging commenced. We labored six hours a day, digging out the immense hole, all by hand. Eastman took the project to heart and was raring to go each and every morning. Of course, he did little more than stand around issuing orders, as we performed the wearisome manual labor.

Right from the very beginning it was suggested that the use of a bulldozer would expedite the work and ease our burden; however, the suggestion was never heeded, or more likely, within the realm of Eastman's mentality, was never passed on to the CO.

We toiled day after day on that superfluous task. Every inch was coercibly dug with sweat and agony. Although we still had gun duty at night, we were able to relinquish the radio watch to Mailer, Eastman, and Lybin. That was of some consequence to us anyway.

The final desired configuration was a fifteen foot square hooch. In order to end up with the walls of this hooch below ground, as it was intended, it was necessary to dig eight feet into the earth. It took many weeks to complete the digging. The most difficult phase of the project was leveling the floor of the excavation before the reconstruction could begin. It was all done by eye.

One week into the feeble-minded project, Ned's flight date came in, freeing him from the drudgery of Captain Drew's folly. That afternoon we ended work on the hooch early and scurried around attempting to scrounge up some beer and a couple of bottles of gook rum for a farewell party for Ned. Not only did we bid farewell to a comrade in arms, but we indulged in some sorely needed therapeutic unwinding, too.

In my case, so much so that I became totally ossified after consuming a canteen cup full of rum and God only knows how many cans of lukewarm beer. The morning after, I awoke sprawled out on my rack and felt like death warmed over. My brain was in a state of suspended animnation and it had no control, whatsoever, over my body. I made a sincere effort to force my eyelids ajar, but they hardly moved, feeling like iron curtains. Through the slits, I desperately tried to focus, but couldn't hold them open. Then, I must have lapsed back into unconsciousness.

Sometime later, when Eastman noticed that I was not at the site working, he dispatched Lou and Al to fetch me. I was in such a stupor that they had to physically assist me out of my rack and with one on each side of me literally carry me back with them. Eastman took one look at me and ordered them to return me to the hooch so that I could sleep it off. I woke up twenty-four hours later with one of the worst hangovers ever.

During the period of reconstruction, the monsoon season remained capricious, and occasionally the rains hampered the progress—to everyone's delight. Nevertheless, the work continued, though sluggishly at best.

Captain Drew somehow managed to procure a meager supply of corrugated steel engineering planks for use as the roofing material. They were a scarce commodity and next to impossible to acquire. Even so, they arrived one day on a supply run from battalion.

For the first time, the CO made an appearance at the construction site to inspect our progress. Although, in reality, he was merely eager to have us complete the hooch prior to the arrival on the hill of several high-ranking field grade officers. I suppose he felt his presence would have accomplished that.

Scuttlebutt had it that the officers were gathering to plan out the logistics of a major operation that was in the offing. They were due to arrive shortly, and Captain Drew needed some place to billet them.

Eastman ordered us to redouble our efforts in order to have it done in time. After the steel planking was set in place, a layer of thin plastic sheets were put down, and finally sandbags were piled on top to complete the job. Because of the pressure he placed on us to finish, the roof was constructed in a haphazard fashion, and the resulting fiasco was not only inevitable, but was the coup de grace as well.

When the officers and their aides arrived, Captain Drew placed the newly constructed hooch at their disposal and they utilized it for their sleeping quarters. As luck would have it, that night we were deluged with a torrential rain and the hastily built roof leaked like a sieve. I would not have wanted to be in Captain Drew's place for all the tea in China, not with so many top brass wanting a piece of him.

That experience fortunately saved the integrity of our remaining hooches. Consequently, Captain Drew promptly shit-canned his brilliant idea and adamantly vowed his revenge.

Not long after that episode did Brunnell stumble in the door of the hooch, guffawing so hysterically that he could barely speak. "What's so humorous?" Al asked, as an infectious smirk sprang across his face.

When Brunnell was able to gain control of himself he gasped, "Captain Drew!" and started laughing again.

"What about him?" Oliver chuckled.

With a sardonic grin he related, "I was in the shitter when Drew came in and sat down. He didn't say anything to me at first, but a couple of minutes later I saw him glance around, looking for a roll of shit paper. When he didn't find any, he looked at me kind of pissed like and asked me, 'Where's the toilet paper? You guys are supposed to maintain this place!' I didn't say anything; I just reached in my pocket, pulled out some C-rat paper, showed it to him, and said, 'I have mine!' wiped my ass and sashayed out. I left him still sitting there with nothing!"

Brunnell couldn't help from letting out a sidesplitting roar. By that time, we too were all in hysterics. Just at that moment, I heard the door of the shitter slam and caught a glimpse of Captain Drew, red as a beet, stomping back up the road. There was no doubt he plainly overheard every word of Brunnell's story, for the shitter was only across the road from our hooch. Lou managed to compose himself long enough to exhort, "Well, I suppose he got the message. . . . Maybe next time when we tell the supply sergeant we're out of shit paper he'll requisition some!"

Whenever there was an opening in the squad it was usually accepted practice to move each subordinate member up in position. That very condition became necessary once Ned rotated. I was slated to move up to the gunner position; however, I made my desire known to Vic that I wanted to remain the A-gunner and that he should consider Lou for the gunner instead. I much preferred A-gunning. I guess you could say that I got my rocks off dropping rounds. My request was perfectly acceptable to Vic. Although Sergeant Mailer did some balking at the idea, he finally relented. In the end, Lou was elevated to gunner and I continued as A-gunner. It was a combination that over the next few months worked exceedingly well.

A navy corpsman was attached to our company, and it was his job to render medical aid to those of us in need. I never actually knew what his surname was, but like everyone else I addressed him as Doc. He was a slight man in physical stature, but towered over others when it came to genuine compassion for others. At first glance he looked considerably older than his twenty years revealed—a consequence directly attributed to his vocation. He, like all his counterparts, was an indispensable part of a grunt company and the first to be called upon when someone was wounded or maimed in combat. Continually dealing with the physical wounds and suffering of others took extraordinary fortitude and courage—much more than I could have mustered. It was not unusual for Doc to demonstrate more concern for those that were wounded than for himself.

In spite of his profession, he carried a sawed-off shot gun, along with his medical pouch. At times I had to wonder who was more gung ho: Doc or us?

Up to this point, I had not required Doc's services, and thankfully so. However, it had become necessary when I developed several tiny blisters directly below my left eye, near the bridge of the nose. When they began to spread after several days, I became somewhat alarmed and had Doc take a look. He examined me and quickly diagnosed me as being infected with sandworm: a condition closely related to ringworm. He told me that it was common and not to be overly concerned about it. He figured that I most likely had transmitted it by rubbing my eye with dirty hands.

Unfortunately, he was not able to treat it himself and sent me to the battalion aid station. There it was promptly treated using a direct application of liquid nitrogen, whereby it cleared up nicely within a few days, just like Doc said it would.

In the dead of night, two weeks after Ned had rotated, I was up in the tower with Ken when the tower took a few sniper rounds. Two rounds whizzed by our heads. Instinctively, we dove for the floor. "Shit! What the hell was that!" cried Ken.

"I don't fuckin' know, but I'm going down on the gun," I said. I was trembling as I crawled on my stomach over to the doorway and quickly scrambled down the stairs in a crouched sprint. The darkness made it impossible to see more than a foot in front of me as I raced down the hill past the newly constructed hooch. I detected, too late, the presence of another person running directly on a collision course with me and was totally helpless in avoiding the resulting encounter. My forward momentum was such that the ensuing crash knocked me off balance and I continued stumbling forward, desperately trying to stay on my feet. Nevertheless, I lost the battle and tumbled onto the muddy road. In one continuous motion I rolled back to my feet and finally made it to the gun pit in a fit of anger. I wasn't physically injured, only my pride was hurt. I hadn't the slightest inkling who it was that I had run into, nor did I have time to worry about it.

It seemed like the entire hill had opened up in the direction that the sniper rounds had emanated from. First Platoon positioned themselves along the west side of the hill and began laying down a barrage of fire toward the ville, as did our guns, the 105 battery, the .30 caliber machine guns mounted on the two amtracks parked above the crest of the hill, and the .50 caliber machine gun mounted on a bunker directly opposite our gun pit. During the minute or two of total chaos, someone had been spraying bullets just inches over our heads in the gun pit. It came from the bunker across the road. All of us hit the dirt as orange tracers from the .50 caliber machine guns sliced through the air above us. "Cease fire! Cease fire, you dumb fuck!" Lou lashed out in a rage. "What the hell are you trying to do? Blow us away?"

Lou was on his way out of the gun pit when I grabbed his arm and held him back. "Calm down, Lou!" I insisted.

"Why the hell should I? That dumb son of a bitch almost killed us all!" he screamed contemptuously, yanking his arm from my grip.

"It's over, man. . . . It's over," I said, steering him away from the direction of the bunker.

"Man, I'm going on R&R to Bangkok in two days. I don't need this shit!" stormed Lou.

"As soon as this is over I'm going to find out who that asshole was and get his ass straightened right the fuck out!" Vic snarled furiously.

Seconds later, someone came running down the line crying out, "Hold your fire! Cease fire!"

I couldn't make out who it was. It was too dark out to discern more than a shadow. After several thousand rounds, it was over. We secured the gun and returned to the hooch.

Once inside, the recently installed light bulb in the center of the room revealed the results of my earlier bought with the unknown assailant. The fresh pair of jungles I had put on after my shower were covered with mud, the snap on my holster had been broken off, and my .45 automatic was packed in muck. As I was relating my mishap to Lou, in an effort to divert his anger, Oliver came in laughing. He began telling about running into someone and knocking him over on the way up to his gun pit. I jumped up from my rack and pointed at him in disbelief. "It was you! You son of a bitch!" I shouted. "What the fuck were you running up on the road for? Look what you did to me!" I tugged at my jungles and held up my mud-caked, holstered .45 automatic. Oliver just stood there with a grin from ear to ear displaying his pearly whites and said nothing. "The next time at least smile. . . . That way maybe I'll see ya coming!" I cracked sarcastically.

"I'm sorry, man. I didn't know it was you, Ski. Honestly! I didn't want to stay around. I thought whoever it was was going to get up and come after me."

"Well, what the hell were you doing on the road anyway? You know your supposed to use the path along the barbed wire up to the other gun pit." I began to laugh when I thought about how comical it must have looked.

"Sorry, Ski. Did you get hurt?"

"No, just my ego," I chuckled. With that, everyone in the hooch broke out in laughter. Even Lou permitted a smile to penetrate his infuriated scowl.

A faint rumble grew louder and louder, until the whopping of chopper blades cutting the air became conspicuous. Several of us ran from the hooch into the pitch blackness of the night. The noise became deafening and the dust started whipping up from the road. It seemed as though an invisible chopper was hovering over head. Finally, I could barely discern the shadowy shape of a '34. Suddenly, I felt a heart-sinking feeling when I realized it was going to land on the roof of our hooch. Lou shouted hysterically for everyone to get out just as its landing light flashed on for an instant. The pilot immediately veered off and aborted the landing. His navigation lights had been turned off prior to his approach of the hill. It was standard procedure when attempting a night landing in a hostile area. But why was he landing here?

No sooner asked than was the answer at hand. A marine carrying a red strobe light and a radio man dashed by us toward the makeshift LZ. They were followed by two more carrying a stretcher with someone wincing in pain. The chopper made another approach and was safely guided in by the strategically placed strobe. It was down for only a few seconds. The four marines cleared the blades and the '34 was airborne once again, heading for Da Nang. We later learned someone had an appendicitis attack that required immediate hospitalization; hence the need for a medivac chopper in the middle of the night. Boy, was I glad the pilot had enough good sense to switch on his light and check where he was landing. It would have been quite tragic had he not. Afterward, we all joked about it. Just a nervous reaction, I guess. It certainly wasn't a joking matter. God must have surely been watching out for our best interests that night.

Two days after Lou departed for his R&R, Sergeant Mailer quickly hobbled to our gun pit dressed in a clear pair of camouflage utilities, with gun belt, .45 automatic, and all. I turned to Vic and said, "Hey! Something's up!"

When Mailer reached the side of the gun pit, he hurriedly ordered, "Get yourselves and the gun squared away! A reporter and photographer from the *Stars and Stripes* are here on the hill and they'll be down here soon to do a story on eighty-ones."

"Hey, how about that!" cried Al, pleased at the thought.

"Just what we need!" said Vic, with a frown.

Mailer had already turned and was heading back when I quipped, "All dressed up for the big occasion, huh, Sarge?" He made no effort to respond other than flipping his middle finger into the air.

"I don't know why you keep antagonizing him for, Ski," Vic groused. "You just get him pissed off and he takes it out on everybody else." I just shrugged my shoulder and flashed a perfidious smile in reply.

A few minutes later Al said, "I guess that's them up by the tower with Captain Drew."

We all stood on the ammo bunker and watched as the photographer took some pictures of the CO and some others. They talked for a while, and then Sergeant Mailer escorted them down to our gun pit. After he introduced each of us, the reporter asked for the spelling of our names and ranks. A few pictures were snapped of us at the gun, and several questions were asked about what we did. Al inquired, "Are you really going to print those pictures?"

"You bet, marine!" answered the reporter. And with that they said good-bye and trotted up the hill toward the CO's bunker.

"Boy, is Lou going to be full of envy when he gets back," stated Vic.

"Yeah, just wait till he sees our pictures in the *Stars and Stripes* and he's not in it! He's going to be jealously dancing all over the place," I snickered, in devilish delight.

Vic thought inquisitively for a moment and then muttered, "You know, for the life of me I can't figure out why so much fuss is made over Captain Drew. Why the hell do so many colonels, and even a genreal or two, come out to this out-of-the-way fire base just to see *him*? What the fuck?. . . . Is his old man the commander in chief or what?"

8. Second Operation

A gray curtain of torrential rain rapidly converged on our hill from the east. When viewed from our vantage point, one could almost estimate—in minutes—how soon the rain would engulf the hill. Suddenly, raging streams of muddy water cascaded along the road in front of our hooch and ever-widening pools began to form around the base plates of the guns, completely submerging them. Drainage ditches had to be dug in order to direct the flow of water out of the gun pits. It soon became hopelessly evident that keeping dry was an exercise in futility.

The monsoon was erratic and capricious. One minute the heavens would unleash their fury and in the next the sun's heat would arduously work at reversing their effect. For extended periods of time—days, weeks, sometimes more—the rains were relentless. Rapidly dwindling endurance and gradually escalating despair were the direct results. There was no time-out called because of the devastating rains; the war only became frustratingly more difficult. Their effects lingered from May to November. The rains, too, were an added burden on the local villagers, who evacuated to high ground before the onslaught arrived each season.

Lou returned from his R&R soaked to the skin on the last day of October—a day before the roads became impassable. Having arrived fresh and invigorated from his all too brief reprieve, he related his amorously pleasant experiences and brought a slight glimmer to the dreariness we all felt.

We became isolated when the roads completely washed out. One could only venture off the hill in a boat, for the low-lying areas were totally under water. By the end of the first week, the rains had subsided; however, the roads remained flooded, which effectively stymied any resupply effort by truck. The chow hall began to scrape the bottom of the barrel of their supplies, and we resorted to C-rats more often than trekking to the chow hall. Luckily, we received an ample resupply of ammo just prior to the flooding or we would have been in a bind as well.

That night, a waning moon beautifully reflected off the mirrorlike body of water surrounding our hill. It had the same illuminating effect as does a moonlit night after a freshly fallen snow. It appeared deceptively peaceful and serene.

Within a day and a half, the rains returned as pesistent as ever. One evening, shortly after nightfall, we came under mortar attack. Two rounds harmlessly exploded in quick succession on the side of the hill, showering mud and debris over the rear of our hooch. We immediately manned the guns in the pouring rain. Even though we donned our rain gear, within a matter of seconds we were totally drenched. The telltale thump made when a mortar round is fired was undetectable in the violent downpour. "Anybody see a muzzle flash out there?" cried Vic, as he stood holding the gun pit phone to his right ear.

"Those explosions sounded like sixty mike-mikes to me. . . . But where the hell could they be coming from? . . . Everything's under water for as far as I can see!" I screamed in frustration.

"Sixty's only have a range of about two clicks!" yelled Lou.

"I know! So where the hell are they firing from?" I replied, as

I climbed on top of the ammo bunker to get a better view. It was raining so hard that the visibility was considerably reduced. Just then another round struck the hill, dead center on the road, between us and the 175-mm battery. "See anything . . . any flashes?" Vic called, with his hands cupped over his mouth.

"No! I don't see any fuckin' thing except water! They must be in a boat somewhere out there," I shouted back, wiping the rain from my face.

Suddenly, Vic yelled, "We've got a fire mission coming in!"

After firing several rounds in the direction of the southern end of the hill, I still had no idea what it was that we were firing at. The rain was so heavy during that time that I had to take the time out to pull the tube from the base plate, dump the accumulated rainwater, and then resume firing. We evidently were firing at various suspected locations but never knew for certain if we had found our intended target. Shortly after, the attack ceased.

For the next several days, the sun reappeared and the flooding began to reside, leaving in its wake boggish mud where roads had been before. This condition necessitated resupply by chopper, which came to our rescue in the nick of time, for we were dangerously low on both provisions and ammo. A steady stream of UH-34s made the resupply run to our hill.

Once on the ground, the fresh supplies had to be carted off to the proper areas on the hill. Luckily, our area was located close to the LZ. Everyone else was situated on the other side of the hill and consequently had the added difficulty of plodding through boot-deep mud. What normally would have been a simple task was rendered pure drudgery. A human chain was formed from the LZ to the crest of the hill and the supplies were passed along from man to man. There was a lighter side too. Every so often someone lost his balance and ended up wallowing in the muck. Hours later, the exhausted and mud-bedecked human supply line was finally ended.

A bundle of *Stars and Stripes* was included with the resupply, and we grabbed several for ourselves. Fully prepared to banter Lou, Vic skimmed through the pages in search of our picture, but found only one of Captain Drew. It depicted him alone, training his .45 automatic at the head of a captured VC, who was squatting on the ground and blindfolded. The caption read, "Captain Drew captures Viet Cong single-handed!"

"I don't believe this shit!" cried Vic, pointing to the picture at the top of page three. "Would you look at this!"

"What the hell?" Oliver exclaimed, as he peered at the picture. "Where does he get off posing for a picture like that?"

"What are you guys talking about?" I asked.

"Turn to page three and you'll see," said Vic.

"No shit! Isn't that the gook First Platoon brought in? Drew wasn't even out on that patrol when they captured him!" I balked.

"Yeah, and wait till those guys see that picture. . . . Boy, are they going to be pissed!" said Oliver.

The news spread over the hill like wildfire. Before long, everyone was in an uproar, for the very thought was a total and utterly contrived travesty of truth. Not only First Platoon, but everyone else in the company was infuriated to think that the reporter would have intentionally—or more likely, unknowingly—misrepresented the facts to bolster Captain Drew's image. But why? Were there political aspirations on his horizon? One could only speculate about this, for he hadn't even made a feeble attempt at an explanation.

Someone had been baffling our new company gunnery sergeant, who, in addition to his usual duties, had also assumed the responsibility of supply sergeant. For a period of time, various supplies had been found missing. The gunny had discovered a note inside the locked company supply hooch, which was intentionally left behind by the intruder. The note read, "The Phantom strikes again." That infuriated the gunnery sergeant and prompted him to place two large padlocks on the door. Of course, we all came under suspicion, since eighty-ones were in such close proximity to the supply hooch. It was just across the road from the our FDC. Although the gunnery sergeant ardently questioned us, he had no real evidence.

After the new locks failed as a deterrent, the gunnery sergeant took more drastic measures—or so he thought. He booby-trapped the only door and window by wiring them with hand flares in order to catch the filcher in the act. To the gunny's dismay, the flares failed to announce the culprit's presence. Again, a similar message was left inside, but this time the gunnery sergeant had found some physical evidence. It appeared as though a utility hat, with a name inside, was inadvertently dropped by the then infamous and intriguing Phantom. Had he become careless?

We weren't privy to the name found in the hat until the gunnery sergeant conducted his investigation. Then, through the grapevine, we learned that the name inside the hat was Slack. Unfortunately, that only proliferated the mystery. Slack had rotated several months before. It couldn't possibly have been him; however, my personal suspicions had been confirmed, for I was probably the only one who knew that Slack had given Brunnell one of his utility hats before he departed. That piece of substantial evidence coupled with Brunnell's innate ability to forage around and come up with the most unlikely items, proved to me beyond a shadow of a doubt that he was indeed the Phantom.

I dared not approach Sergeant Mailer with what I knew or Brunnell would surely have been doing a stint in the Long Binh jail. Instead, at an opportune time, I laid it all out for Vic and he agreed.

"We have to do something about getting the heat off of our section," said Vic.

"Yeah, but what?" I challenged.

"I don't know! But we better have a serious talk with Brunnell first; then we can go from there."

"Good idea," I said, with an affirmative nod. "Let's talk to him right after chow tonight."

118

"Okay. The sooner the better."

On that particular day, the Corps turned 193 years old. November 10 has always been a day of special meaning to all marines—on active duty or otherwise. The fact that we were in combat on the Corp's birthday only heightened our feelings of comradeship and "esprit de corps."

Even the chow hall treated us to a very special dinner at the evening meal. All who entered its portals that night were greeted with a printed menu, listing the evening's fare. It was literally a soup to nuts meal. Beef consume and tomato juice were served as an appetizer. A baked ham with all the trimmings was the main course, complimented with freshly baked, piping hot rolls, real mashed potatoes instead of the usual rice, an assortment of vegetables garnished with herbs, fresh milk instead of powdered, and for dessert there was a choice of Jell-O with fruit or chocolate pudding. Then, of course, there were the nuts. Not only did the feast delight our taste buds and exemplify the cook's culinary skills, but also more importantly it was an excellent meal—it was that something extra with which to celebrate our birthday.

Those not fortunate enough to be near a chow hall that day were not forgotten either. Every effort was made to get them a hot meal also.

On the way back from chow that night, Vic and I cornered Brunnell alone. Brunnell was somewhat reluctant at first, but was easily persuaded once he was confronted with the facts. He told us that he had elected not to involve anyone else and hence the reason for remaining silent. Brunnell assured us that he would cease his pilfering and not mention it to a soul, only after we impressed upon him the consequences of his actions. "I have only one nagging question. . . . "

"How did I get in without tripping the flares?" Brunnell said, cutting me short.

"Yeah! How did you?" I asked, with great curiosity.

"Yeah, how? I'd like to know too!" chimed Vic.

"It was simple! You know how the far side of the supply hooch is all above ground where the door and window is? . . . and the side facing us and the road is just about all under the ground?"

"Yeah," Vic and I both answered in unison.

"And you know how the roof slants down toward the road and how it's sandbagged on top?" he asked, as he motioned diagonally downward in the air with his hand.

Again we both nodded our heads at the same time. "Well, right there where the roof meets the road I just lifted up the corner of the roof and climbed in. Simple!" he said, raising his eyebrows, as his eyes widened.

"Holy shit! You mean to tell us that the roof's not nailed down?" Vic asked in disbelief.

"Nope!" he answered, shaking his head.

"Well, I'll be damned! So that's how you did it." I said, still stunned by the simplicity.

"I've never been in there. Is there anything good? Never mind. Don't answer that. . . . I'd rather not know!" said Vic.

The investigation dragged on for several days as Vic and I kept a close watch on Brunnell, making sure he stayed clear of the supply hooch. We knew that we needed something to dispel the shadow of suspicion cast on our two squads, when finally at gun drill the next day it was a godsend. The solution presented itself. There we were running gun drill when the resupply truck pulled in and the driver and his helper began unloading the new supplies into the supply hooch; however, at the same time they were pilfering things from inside and secreting them in the cab of the truck. A big smile instantly sprang over Vic's face. I knew just what he was thinking. He sent Al to fetch the gunnery sergeant so he could see for himself. When he arrived, by way of sneaking around the far side of the gun pit so that he wouldn't be seen, he was outraged to discover the two of them stealing supplies that they had delivered previously.

The next day, not only did the gunnery sergeant apologize,

but as a reconciliatory gesture he issued all of us in eighty-ones two First Marine Division sweat shirts each, before anyone else in the company was issued one. We never did find out what fate awaited the two unfortunate patsies; however, Vic and I felt little remorse, for all's fair in love and war. Brunnell was off the hook and he owed us one.

My stateside combat boots finally deteriorated to a point where they were no longer serviceable. The black leather had turned a dirty brown color with the lack of shoe polish, both heels had torn loose and flopped about freely as I walked. I was in desperate need of a new pair. Knowing that Brunnell always had a good supply of most things, I turned to him and asked, "Hey, Brunnell, do you happen to have an extra pair of boots that I can borrow until I can get a new pair of my own?"

"Ahh, what size do you wear?" he asked.

"Ten," I answered.

"Sure! No sweat!" he willingly volunteered.

After digging under his rack, he pulled out a brand new pair of jungle boots and handed them to me, saying, "Here, they're yours! And you don't have to worry about returning them."

"Thanks! But that's okay; I will as soon as I get to battalion supply."

"No, no! I insist! Keep them," he said with forceful gratitude.

So I did!

Rumors of a short walk in the sun soon preoccupied everyone's thoughts, including the gunnery sergeant's. Battalion's S2 received information that there was a large staging of NVA about five clicks out from our hill. It was the general consensus that we would be deployed to engage them—and we were.

Once again we prepared our gear for another operation. Along with the preparations, our anxieties swiftly mounted. The plan of attack, as it was related to us, was scheduled to begin at the break of dawn. As it happened, we were choppered out as the sun's rays began to penetrate the early morning mist. We were inserted four clicks out on Hill 10. From there, we had to hump it one more click to our final destination—a second Hill 10. Most of us had the same question circulating in our minds: Why were we not choppered all the way out there? The answer was simple: our final destination had been targeted as a hot LZ. No one flew into that type of situation willingly and knowingly, unless the circumstances dictated the need.

With the entire company safely on the ground, we moved out quietly at a steady pace, single file, along the side of the road. As the morning wore on we swept through ville after ville, expecting contact at any moment. It was tremendously nerve racking. There was very little to keep one company, except for one's own private thoughts, the view of the man in front of them, and the sounds one's own boots made as one drudged along. I constantly played it out in my mind what action I would take if we were suddenly ambushed. There were so many variables that one couldn't plan an action for them all. My thoughts were sharply interrupted by the ever-increasing pain from the straps of the ammo board digging into my shoulders and then, too, the added weight of the tube (twenty-three pounds) as I alternated it from shoulder to shoulder.

By late morning, the sun baked off the cool mist and it rapidly took its toll on our bodies. I was popping salt tablets by the handful and rationed myself from my two canteens of water. Only a sip at a time, or it would be gone before I knew it. My faded green T-shirt darkened as it became soaked with sweat, and my helmet produced a steady wave of perspiration down my forehead. Both my ears had an ever-resounding ring in them, and I had to force my legs not to waiver under the load.

As usual, the villagers scarcely threw a glance in our direction as we passed through. Even so, I had a strange feeling we were under close scrutiny every step of the way. A sorely needed ten minute break was finally called and we rested at the side of the road. I nearly collapsed from exhaustion as I bent down, leaned back slightly on my heels, and allowed the weight of my ammo rack to pull me down. Lying there stretched out, I dared not remove the ammo board from my back or the pain would have been excruciating when I had to saddle up again. With the tube cradled in my arms and my helmet pushed forward, shading my eyes from the grueling sun, I took full advantage of every second we had.

Ten minutes vanished like it was ten seconds. Unable to overcome the force of gravity and sit straight up, I had to roll over to stand with the weight of the ammo board strapped to my back. Not the least bit refreshed, we reluctantly moved out. Only this time we departed from the road and made our way over the narrow dikes and through the murky water of the rice paddies.

The word was passed from man to man to fan out as we slowly began to close on Hill 10. Sloshing though the then muddy water of the rice paddies became more difficult with each step. The silt-laden bottom acted like a giant suction, and the weight of my gear only plunged me deeper into the muck. As I waded closer and closer to the hill, the strength in my legs rapidly diminished. It became an all-out struggle to free each foot and to keep from floundering. Straining every bit of energy my body could muster, I kept moving forward.

The same thoughts kept flashing in my mind: Where were the gooks? We were told this was a hot LZ, so why haven't they fired on us yet? Are they waiting until we get closer or have they *didied* out of here when they saw us coming? It soon became evident that there was no one around.

Ahead of me I could see the first few men of the lead element as they reached the foot of the hill. They climbed out of the muck onto firm ground and turned to help those behind them, before going on.

Long before the main body of the company reached the bottom of the hill, the forward element had gone on to reconnoiter the hill. They found it to be absolutely deserted. It was a bit of good fortune, for it would have been most assuredly an uphill battle with many casualties, especially since we were in such a state of fatigue.

I waded up to the waist high embankment and handed over the

tube to an outstretched hand. Next to me I saw Lou with one leg straddled over the embankment, off balance, and straining to get the rest of his body up and over. It would have been an amusing sight had I not been so tired. I placed both hands onto the ground in an attempt to hurl myself up. The first try failed as both feet were steadfastly held by the mud. On the subsequent try I concentrated every last drop of energy on pulling myself out and was able to free my boots, but not enough to make it all the way out. I was dangling on the edge and began sliding back in. Suddenly, I felt someone grab hold of my ammo board from the top and drag me up onto solid ground. For a second I just lay there collecting what little energy I could. Shading my eyes from the intense sun, I found it to be Vic who was standing there holding the tube. "You looked like you needed a hand," Vic said.

"Yeah, I did. Thanks," I mumbled.

"Here's your tube back. I'm going to help Lou out."

Lou was only a few feet away and still in the same position—one leg over the embankment. Vic grabbed hold of his ammo board and tugged on it as Lou struggled over the edge. In the meantime, I crawled over to him to help and clumsily pulled his leg toward me. I was laughing so hard that I was of little help. Vic slipped, landing on his backside, and Lou ended up lying in a prone position on the ground. The three of us were a pathetic sight, indeed.

It was midafternoon by the time the last of the company settled in on Hill 10. A perimeter was installed around the hill, a command post hastily set up, foxholes dug, and our guns set in. We were prepared for whatever the gooks had in store for us that night. We were all certain it would come. The only questions were: where, when, and how hard?

Both guns were laid in, approximately thirty meters apart on the only level area of the hill. Two-hour gun watches were assigned, with one man on each gun. I drew the 2400-to-0200-hour watch, figuring that we would get hit during that time or shortly after. At least I would get several hours of uninterrupted sleep first.

Conversations were kept to a minimun, and most of us sacked out as twilight slowly faded into darkness. A brightly glowing moon low in the western sky made it easy for us to see what we were doing, but by the same token it had the adverse effect of illuminating us and making us easy targets.

No sooner had I dozed off than was I startled awake by the relentless attack of a swarm of red ants. Not fully conscious, I began swatting my legs instinctively as my brain recognized the sensation of being bitten repeatedly. Realizing that I had been lying on an anthill, I grabbed my utility hat, jumped up, and continued flailing away at them. All the commotion I had made woke up the others. As soon as they saw me dancing around swatting myself, they recognized the problem and immediately came to my aid. They too began swatting the ants as they scurried around incessantly biting at me. It felt like my legs were on fire. When I was finally rid of them all, I stripped off my trousers and shook them out just to be sure. They were called fire ants—not only for their color, but for their fierce and easily provoked bite. Apparently, I had chosen to sleep on their home and they were merely defending it. By the time it was all over with, everyone was awake and had a good laugh at my expense. I moved to a different spot and carefully inspected it for anthills prior to sacking out again.

My prediction was right on the money. My watch dragged on without incident, but an hour into the next watch the gooks probed the far side of the hill. Several small explosions were immediately answered with machine gun and small arms fire from the grunts on that side. Within a matter of seconds, the entire company was up and scrambling around. There was still some shouting going on after the firing ceased. Then a call for a corpsman was faintly heard in the distance. Someone got hit.

Several minutes later, the firing broke out again in the same area, and we were called upon to fire illumination high over the tree line. Setting the illumination fuses for the maximum setting, we fired one every twenty seconds for the next full minute. Thirty seconds later, a second call came for three rounds of HE to be fired into the same tree line. Al and Brunnell broke out the rounds and handed them to me one at a time. When Lou had the gun up, I dropped each down the tube as fast as I could. Only seconds passed when three consecutive explosions rattled the tree line. A slight odor of cordite lingered in the air, and then quiet returned to the hill.

Morning broke with a damp mist clinging close to the ground, and the sky was becoming increasingly overcast. That meant only one thing—rain was most certainly on its way. A quick count of our ammo showed that our supply was down to almost nothing. It was a precarious position to be in. Both guns were thoroughly cleaned after morning chow, and the ammo situation was reported to the CP. We also learned that the only casualty from the night before was a guy from Third Platoon who took a piece of shrapnel in the ankle. It wasn't a million dollar wound, but enough for a Purple Heart.

At midmorning, First and Third Platoons were sent out on patrol, while Second Platoon remained behind to provide security for the hill. Our FO and radio man went along with them. Unfortunately, our guns would be of little use until we were resupplied with ammo.

With all of our chores out of the way, we had little else to do but wait around. It wasn't long before the sound of droning engines were heard approaching from the north and paper bullets began raining from the sky. Thousands of them floated aimlessly over the entire area. They were *Chieu Hoi* leaflets intended for the enemy soldiers. In their own language each leaflet described our open arms program and promised financial aid and clemency to those who stopped fighting and turned themselves in. Others offered monetary rewards for various weapons turned in to the South Vietnamese government. Still others described how their services could be offered as Kit Carson scouts. It was just another tactic we employed to disrupt the enemy and sway any malcontents among them by other than forceful means.

Before we knew it, the resupply chopper had arrived and eighty-ones were detailed to unload it. In addition to the 81-mm ammo, we were also supplied with C-rats and boxes of small arms ammo, both 5.56-mm and 7.62-mm. After many trips back and forth from the LZ to our guns, we finally finished carrying all fifteen boxes of HE, ten boxes of illumination, and two boxes of WP. Each box weighed somewhere in the neighborhood of thirty pounds. Then came the task of breaking out the ammo. It was a mundane procedure that anyone of us could do in our sleep—break open the wooden boxes, dump out the canisters into a common location, tear off the tape that sealed the tops, slide out the round, remove the packing, replace it in the canister, and finally stack the ammo in the bunker. Over the past seven months if I had done that once, I did it a thousand times.

No sooner had we finished stacking the ammo than a fire mission was called in. Seconds after the gun was set on the aiming stakes, one round of WP erupted with a yellowish flash followed by the sound of a dull thud in a dense stand of trees. The resulting plume of white smoke drifted skyward above the foliage. No correction was required, and it was followed up with a request to fire three rounds of HE for effect. They too were fired off and struck in perfect alignment within the target area. After the rounds were fired, we were instructed to secure the gun. Then there wasn't much else to do but wait.

Just prior to dusk, both platoons had made their way back to the hill and were replaced with several ambush patrols from Second Platoon for the night. Before they left the hill, their platoon sergeant and our FO collaborated and plotted H&I's at strategic points throughout their areas of operation.

Like the night before, gun watches were set up. Only this time we had to fire H&I's every half hour, which at least broke the monotony. By choice I drew the same watch as I had the previous night.

We all gathered around the guns and shot the breeze before turning in. The moon slowly sank below the horizon early in the evening, as threatening storm clouds rapidly rolled in. It was obvious we were in for a wet night. I covered the gun with its poncho to keep the rain from filling the tube and was the first to turn in.

During the night, a cool, soaking rain roared through like an express train. I awoke as the first few drops struck my face. Soon, sheets of rippling water rushed by me, seeking out the lowest points on the hill. Wrapped in my poncho, I tossed and turned until I was completely covered from the rain. But I fought a losing battle, for there were too many tears in my poncho.

By the time my watch rolled around, the rain had ceased. The base plate of the gun was filled with water, so I bailed it out by hand. Several handfuls emptied most of it out nicely. When that was finished, I set the gun's deflection and elevation to the next series of coordinates and readied one round of HE with a charge four. When it was 0015 hours, I fired the first of four rounds on my watch. The H&I's were intended to harass and interdict the enemy. Other than the earsplitting thump when the round was fired and the distant thud when it exploded, the night was very calm. After firing the last round, I woke up Brunnell for his watch. When he was up and I was sure he was awake, I turned in.

By morning, the ground had soaked up all the water like a sponge, except beneath where I slept. There, it was still quite damp, and so was I.

As planned, the ambush patrols returned to the hill at daybreak. They had zero contact the entire night and were soaked to the skin, tired, and hungry. It was apparent that the gooks once again chose to flee instead of standing their ground and fighting it out face-to-face. Their strategy was to whittle us down little by little with hit-and-run tactics and booby traps. Their leaders were quite cognizant of the fact that their forces were no match for our military prowess, and they fought accordingly. It was a frustrating situation for us, but we were flexible and adapted our tactics with moderate success.

That morning, two different rumors circulated around the company. One alluded that the CO wanted to stay out in the boonies for a few more days tracking down the gooks, while the other had us being chopper back to battalion by late morning. As it turned out, four amtracks and a tank arrived in the afternoon to take us back. Why we were taken to battalion and not to Hill 65 was beyond me!

When we arrived at 3/7, it was nearly dark and the cloud-packed heavens once again unloaded their burdens. The entire company was deployed in the trenches surrounding the hill for the night. The only consolation we were afforded was sleep for the entire night, with no need to stand watch.

Prior to taking up the positions our mail was distributed. I received several letters and one package that apparently had been opened and resealed. Attached to it I found a standard post office note indicating that the package had been damaged in shipping. When I opened the package its contents reeked of pickle juice. On further inspection I found a letter tucked inside from my cousin Danny, stating he hoped that I would enjoy the pickles he sent. He and I always had a pickle eating contest at the family Fourth of July picnic each year. And he usually won. It made me chuckle and brightened my spirits while sitting in a muddy and half-flooded fox hole with my poncho draped over my head and flashlight in hand.

The next morning the same amtracks ferried us back to Hill 65. It was good to be back, but disheartening to find that our hooch had been broken into and some of our personal belongings taken. Corporal Eastman advised us to compile a list of the items missing and submit them to him. He wasn't too clear on just why he wanted us to do that, for we knew full well that we would never get any of it back again.

Vic had his bowie knife taken—he had bought it from me a

few months before for twenty dollars—and was very upset. He always took it with him, and on that particular operation he had forgotten it. Lou had several shirts taken, Al was missing his watch, and Oliver lost his 35-mm camera. I was lucky; only my picture of Raquel Welch was taken from the wall next to my rack.

When the others went to the FDC to turn in their lists, I also went along just to bust balls. Corporal Eastman looked up when it was my turn and very seriously asked, "What are you missing, Ski?"

I cleared my throat and with a straight face answered, "My picture of Raquel Welch!"

A sudden rage filled his eyes and he screamed, "What? Are you *dinky dow?* Get the hell out of here!"

"But . . . you wanted to know what was taken, didn't you?"

"Out! Get out!" he spat.

"Okay, but I was very attached to that picture," I said as I ducked to avoid being hit with the helmet he threw in my direction. As I darted out of the FDC hooch, the others were outside laughing hysterically.

On our way back to the hooch, Vic said, "One of these times Eastman's going pay you back, Ski. You know what they say about pay back!"

"Yeah, I know," I chuckled. "Pay back is a motherfucker!"

That night I found that a family of rats had invaded our hooch while we were away. I first discovered them when one scampered across my chest during the night. It scared the hell out of me, and then I couldn't get back to sleep. Several of them continued to scurry around the ledge formed where the ammo box walls met the roof on the inside of the hooch. It was a perfect raceway for them to get around from one side of the hooch to the other. I woke up Oliver to borrow his rat trap and set it on the ledge baited with a small piece of cracker. Then, in the darkness, I lay in my rack and waited to hear it snap. Within a matter of seconds I heard little footsteps patter along the ledge to the trap. There was a short silence and then away they went again. I trained my flashlight on the trap and found it empty, but still set. "Why that smart little fuckin' rat stole the bait! Maybe I didn't set the tension light enough. I'll try it again," I mumbled to myself.

I played around with it until I thought that I had the tension right; then I carefully slid the trap back on the ledge and gingerly placed a small piece of cracker in it. Whack! It almost got my finger in the process. I tried it again, only this time I placed the bait in it before I had set it; then I gently slid it back on the ledge and waited again. Just like before, little foot steps raced along from about midway around the hooch, over to the trap. I followed the sound with my eyes but couldn't discern even the slightest shape in the dark. A few minutes passed and I heard it scurry away, but this time in the other direction. "What the hell . . . " I thought.

When I looked, it was empty again. By that time I had become totally annoyed with the rat. I decided that a whole cracker was needed. It couldn't possibly snatch out something that big without setting off the trap. Well, I was wrong! A few minutes later I heard the cracker being dragged along the ledge. When I shined the light on it, the little rodent dropped the cracker and quickly fled along the ledge to the other side. I needed to find another solution to the dilemma. Then it dawned on me to try some peanut butter instead of the cracker, so I did. And that did the trick. With the same glob of peanut butter I succeeded in trapping nine rats, although I stayed up half the night doing so. Everyone else in the hooch was oblivious to my little hunting endeavor and slept through the whole time. Nevertheless, as tired as I was, when morning rolled around I was proud to display my personal body count for everyone to see.

For the next full week, Brunnell was assigned to mess duty. On the first day he returned just after dark. Seconds before he entered the hooch, a powerfully rancid stench filtered through the doorway. Brunnell had been detailed to clean the grease pit behind the chow hall and had to climb down into the slimy muck at the bottom. Brunnell was immediately thrown out of the hooch and warned not to return before he got rid of his clothes and took a shower. His clothes were completely ruined and had to be burned the next day.

Each night thereafter, for the remainder of the week, Brunnell managed to bring some leftovers back with him. One night he brought back two loaves of bread and a whole bologna. We had a field day filling ourselves with a midnight snack of baloney sandwiches and grog made from twelve packets of assorted Kool-Aid flavors in five gallons of water—which proved to be sheer agony on the stomach the next morning.

9.   Relocation

The usually unforgiving monsoon season grudgingly provided us with a considerable respite, although threatening skies were ever constant. We were not at all unhappy to have been rid of the rain, for it was one less element with which we had to contend with—and God only knew we had plenty to contend with without it.

For the second time in November, the chow hall succeeded in skillfully demonstrating their culinary talents. They prepared the most superb Thanksgiving Day dinner that I have ever tasted while in the Corps: turkey with all the traditional side dishes—thyme stuffing, turkey gravy, mashed potatoes, yams, cornbread, and cranberry sauce. As if that wasn't enough, there was also a selection of pumpkin, minced, or apple pie a la mode for dessert. Needless to say, I left the chow hall stuffed to my eyeballs.

Later that night, I found myself up in the tower with Ken and Al. Our conversation seemed to focus on reminiscing about how we each celebrated Thanksgiving with our families back in the World. It was difficult not to become misty-eyed and homesick. When it was my turn, I related to them how my grandmother always had our entire family to dinner and how she would begin preparing the turkey early in the morning. The homemade pumpkin and apple pies were prepared the day before. I recalled savoring the invitingly delicious aroma of the turkey cooking in the oven as I stepped through the door of her kitchen. She toiled for hours over the bird with loving care, basting it to a crispy golden brown on the outside and tender on the inside. Next to Christmas, Thanksgiving was my favorite holiday. I anxiously anticipated its arrival each year.

I celebrated my nineteenth birthday, as my eighth month in the country drew to a close. As a birthday present of sorts, November 30 was the day on which Sergeant Mailer was scheduled to rotate.

Two days earlier, he had caught a ride to Da Nang on the admin run and wasn't with us on my birthday. He wasn't all missed! Even before he was gone, we were wondering who his replacement would be. Surely Corporal Eastman wouldn't become the section leader! Only time would tell.

Nineteen was the average age of most of us who were serving in Nam. Interestingly enough, the statistics indicated that we were younger by several years than those who had fought in previous wars. I was sure that the statistics would someday have a significant meaning to those who would inevitably study and analyze the war. It was suggested by some that it was a result of our country's ever changing social fabric. Maybe it was! Nevertheless, whatever the reason was, at the time I really didn't care, nor did it seem to be important to anyone else either.

Rumors began floating around that our battalion would be moving again. This time the scuttlebutt had us transferring areas of operation with First Battalion. The reason that was suggested seemed pointedly valid. First Battalion was judged to be less than effective in holding down their area of operation. (They were strategically positioned just outside of Da Nang.) Consequently, with Tet rapidly approaching and last year's staggering offensive by the enemy still freshly imbued in their memory, Division felt compelled to minimize any possible repetition of last year's initial success by the enemy.

As the days progressed, the rumors persisted and the chances seemed more likely than ever that the transfer would come to pass.

Finally, we were officially informed that we would indeed swap areas of operation with First Battalion. The logistics of such a move necessitated a precise timetable. Our company was scheduled to depart on the morning of December 8.

There was much to do and everything seemed to be happening at once. We were by no means saddened when we heard that Captain Drew had been transferred to division headquarters for the remainder of his tour and that he would be gone before the big move. I was sure that he would be much more comfortable there than out in the boonies with us. Subsequently, little thought was given to who might replace him, for we had no choice in the matter anyway.

It was midmorning when Charlie came racing down the road shouting, "They're having a USO show over at the Oh-five battery! Hey, everybody! Do ya hear me? They're having a USO show!"

He stopped at the gun pit and was boiling over with excitement when he announced the details of the USO show to Al and Brunnell; then he rushed into our hooch, nearly out of breath, and shouted, "There's going to be a USO show at thirteen hundred hours, over at the Oh-five battery! I was just over at my buddy's hooch and got the word."

"Oh, yeah. . . . Who would come all they way out here?" asked Lou, with a skeptical look on his face.

"I don't know—some Australian group is what I heard," he replied in a fluster.

"Sounds outstanding to me," said Vic.

"Me too!" I added enthusiastically.

"Did you tell Corporal Eastman?" asked Vic.

"Sure did! He seemed to have already known about it and said to tell everyone else."

"Ya know . . . this is going to be the first USO show I've ever seen," I said in reflection.

"Yeah, I think that's true for all of us," observed Vic.

"Is Eastman going to let all of us go?" questioned Charlie. "He might just want some of us to stay behind in case of a fire mission."

"No way! Fuck him!" cried Lou. "I'm not missing this for nobody!"

Vic volunteered, "I'll go see him and let him know that we're all going."

"I'll go with you, Vic," I called as he got up to go.

"No!" he said sharply. "You better not; you only agitate him. I'm better off going by myself; that way there's a better chance that he'll agree," directed Vic.

"Okay. I'll wait here," I said, with a wide grin and the proverbial halo over my head.

A few minutes later Vic returned. "No problem," he announced as he walked through the doorway. "He didn't give me a bit of trouble when I told him we're all going. I was kind of surprised!"

"What did he say?" asked Lou.

"He just said it was okay for us to go," Vic answered with a shrug of his shoulders.

"Outstanding! Fuckin' outstanding!" cried Lou.

We moseyed over to the '05 battery's area approximately fifteen minutes before the show started. When we arrived, there must have been almost two hundred marines scattered around the stage area. Some were perched on hooch tops, some were lounging on the ground, and still others were sitting atop a nearby truck. As we wound our way through the sea of green uniforms, Lou and I split from the others and chose the area just to the left of the large wooden platform apparently built for the occasion. It was situated on the inner slope of the hill. Beyond the platform, one could gaze directly out over the multicolored landscape and barely discern the battalion's hill against the distant horizon.

Positioned on the open stage were several folding chairs, a set of drums, three microphones on stands, several sizeable speakers, two massive amplifiers, three electric guitars, and yards of wire connecting everything together.

Minutes later, four guys and a girl, all dressed in civies, bounded onto the makeshift stage and took up their instruments. Their appearance generated instant applause from the entertainment-starved audience. The lone girl was the first round-eyed female I'd seen for quite a few months. She was in her early twenties, short, slightly plump, had fire red, shoulder length hair, and wore a pink, sleeveless minidress. The band leader appeared a little older than the others and sported a goatee. They immediately began playing "I Want To Hold Your Hand" by the Beatles.

When they finished the first song, the audience responded with a prolonged and thunderous applause. Then, when the clamor died down, the lead singer, in a very down-under accent, introduced himself and the others as the Ducans, from Australia. He continued along by introducing each member of the band by name. As they waved we clapped. After the introductions were completed, they went on to play song after song and acted out several comedy skits to our absolute delight. During one skit, the lead singer donned a long blue dress and a curly black wig, impersonating a female. He dashed out into the audience, and while still clutching his microphone, sat on the lap of one of the guys sitting in the front row, and sang him a love song. The poor guy turned red with embarrassment, while everyone else was in stitches. The Ducans concluded their sensational performance with an instrumental arrangement titled "Pipeline."

Three hours of continuous performing, during the most brutal heat of the day, left them haggard looking and exhausted. We extended our overwhelming appreciation by giving them a standing ovation intermingled with hoots, howls, and cheers. After the final curtain call, they remained to answer our questions and then graciously posed for pictures. Everyone with a camera busily clicked away. Of course I couldn't pass up the opportunity to capture a picture of my first USO show for my scrap book. I quickly snapped a few shots as they huddled together off to one side of the stage.

The following day was wet and gloomy. It acted as a grim reminder that the monsoon season was still with us, as we resumed the task of preparing to relocate to our new area of operation. As the day progressed, my cheerful mood, generated by the previous day's USO show, quickly evaporated and I became somewhat doleful about leaving Hill 65. It had been our haven for many long months and I had become very attached to the homyeness it provided. Nevertheless, the day had come for us to saddle up and move out for good.

We collected all of our personal belongings together and staged them on the road in front of our hooch. I had stuffed my ditty bag with odds and ends until it bulged to the point where the zipper wouldn't close. The rest of my gear was crammed into, or attached onto, either my pack or ammo board. Like everyone else, I wore my rifle belt, flak jacket, and helmet, and carried what remained.

Eighty-ones were designated to be transported via amtrack. No sooner had we been advised, than did an amtrack pull up to our gun pit area. Its arrival was nosily preceded by the clangor of its tracks and powerful roar of its engine. It stood idling as it laboriously lowered its forward hatch. The surrounding earth reverberated under our feet. At first glance, the amtrack looked like a giant mechanical monster, with its huge hydraulic hatch held wide open and its empty interior conspicuously visible. A machine gunner sat on top behind a .30 caliber weapon—his position fortified by several rows of sandbags. Next to him was the driver, whose head and shoulders protruded above a small circular hatch.

"You guys ready to load up?" blared the driver over the wailing noise of the engine.

"Ready as we'll ever be!" shouted Corporal Eastman.

The driver flicked a thumbs-up sign, shut down the engine, and emerged from the hatch. He stood atop the amtrack towering high above the ground. Quickly glancing around, he directed his question toward Corporal Eastman. "How much stuff is there?"

"All the gear over there on the road, all the ammo in these bunkers, and all the ammo at the gun pit over there," he replied, pointing to each location in rapid succession.

"Okay, Corporal, let's load up the ammo first."

Eastman turned toward Vic and said, "You heard him. Let's get the ammo on board."

We formed a serpentine line from the bunker to the amtrack and tossed the rounds along from man to man. In no time at all, the bunkers were emptied and the ammo was neatly stacked against the inside wall of the amtrack. Next, our personal gear was stowed on board, including our racks and other miscellaneous items. Lastly, both guns were broken down and placed on board, near the front hatch. One final check was made of the area and we mounted the amtrack.

The driver had to crank the engine a number of times before it started. As he shifted into gear, the fully loaded amtrack lurched forward. The huge, rumbling vehicle lumbered past our hooch to an area wide enough for it to turn around in. Then, slowly, we made our way along the road to the staging area, where we joined the rest of the convoy.

There were many vehicles already assembled around the circumference of the staging area: six-bys, amtracks, tanks, and the CO's jeep with a small trailer attached. Most of the six-bys were loaded with gear and supplies, while the rest of the vehicles were swarmed with flocks of marines.

We made our way through the center area and parked next to another amtrack. From there I watched the gunnery sergeant plod from vehicle to vehicle, instructing the drivers on how the convoy would proceed and what position each should take when we moved out. The ground had been badly churned up by all the tracked vehicles jockeying around, thus making for extremely difficult walking. Twice the gunnery sergeant lost his footing and ended up in a prone position, much to his embarrassment. Brushing off his utilities, he continued on until each driver had received his instructions. Then, gradually, each vehicle fell in line, one behind the other, and the convoy proceeded slowly down the access road, departing Hill 65 for the last time.

A strangely somber mood hung over the squad as we traveled along toward our new destination. Although a few closed their eyes and nodded off, most sat staring out into space with vacant looks in their eyes. As for me, time seemed to stand still as my mind traversed thousands of miles back home. I would rarely allow my thoughts to wander so far away, for it inevitably led to feeling homesick. If one wasn't careful, it could easily worsen and transform into deep despair. Nevertheless, my guard grew weak and I lapsed into deep thought about home. I craved the good times that my friends and I had together as we drove around in an old '59 Plymouth. I remembered how we had to scrounge up our loose change in order to put a few gallons of gas into the car and how the car's AM radio was always blaring away, playing the newest songs on the hit parade. One balmy night, we were cruising around with nowhere special to go, the local radio station was playing "The Sloop John B," and . . .

CRACK!

A sudden jolt to my head snapped me back to reality. In a fraction of a second, I glanced around at the others, scanned the rice paddies, and checked the tree line. I confidently concluded that there was no ominous danger and relaxed my guard slightly. Nobody seemed alarmed or ducked for cover and I was unable to detect any movement along the tree line. Only then did I realize that the amtrack had merely driven through a deep rut in the road and the butt of Oliver's M-16 had slammed into the back of my helmet.

Before very long, the convoy rolled onto an almost barren hilltop that was to become our new fire base. As our amtrack came to a stop, a sudden moderate breeze swept a dense cloud of dust in our direction, adding to the already thick layer that covered everything without exception—nothing escaped. Even my throat was parched from breathing the dust. Losing no time, the company gunnery sergeant called a briefing of the platoon sergeants and our section leader. As for the rest of us, the word was passed to dismount and take a twenty minute break.

Almost a half an hour had passed when Corporal Eastman finally returned. "All right, you guys, listen up! I've been told we are only going to be here temporarily. As soon as the rest of the battalion makes their move, we will be relocating again to the new battalion hill. But that's subject to change, so until then we have to make the best of it—out here!" He paused for a moment, looked around to get his bearings and then continued. "I'm told that our gun pits are located out on the point, right down this road." He pointed. "We'll move down there, get the guns set in and all of our shit squared away before doing anything else."

That entire afternoon we spent doing what we've done hundreds of times before: seating the base plate, laying in the aiming stakes, bore sighting the tube, and stacking ammo. We had a well-disciplined and highly-motivated squad of men—it showed in our teamwork. Everyone knew his job and did it well.

With the work quickly completed, we broke for chow, Brunnell had just returned from the company CP with two cases of C-rats. We all milled around as he tore open the tops of both cases. Like vultures, we each grabbed two meals and settled down to prepare our evening meal. "What did you get, Lou?" I asked, as I sat on the ground next to him.

"Pork and ham and eggs. How about you?"

"Ahhh, turkey and . . . spaghetti with meat balls! Want to trade?" I suggested.

"Yeah! The turkey for the pork?"

"You got it," I said, tossing him the meal marked turkey loaf.

"Shit! I forgot the heat tabs," I said to myself aloud. I began to get up when Lou threw two of them into my lap without saying a word.

"Thanks! But you gave me two! You got enough for yourself?"

"Yup! I took a handful."

141

The two of us sat there on the ground, busily engrossed in preparing our meals. I took out the squatty-shaped cracker can, opened it with a C-rat opener that I kept on my dog tag chain, and proceeded to construct a stove out of it. I made several gashes around the bottom of the can for ventilation and placed a heat tab in the bottom; then I opened the spaghetti can, emptied the contents into my canteen cup, added half a salt packet, a pinch of pepper, a splash or two of water, lit the heat tab, and balanced the cup over the stove. I stirred it gently and every so often had to lift the cup from the flame in order to keep the spaghetti from burning in the bottom.

Everyone had devised their own variations when it came to cooking C-rats. Vic shared one of his with me. He taught me how to jazz up the spaghetti sauce a little by adding a dash or two of Tabasco sauce. Initially, I was reluctant to try it, but I gave in and discovered that it definitely improved the taste. From then on, it became an important part of my recipe.

That night, both squads slept on the guns in anticipation of a welcoming party by the gooks. Being the new occupants of a hill, we half expected our perimeter to be probed, if not hit with an all out ground attack. Nothing materialized.

The next several days were spent lazily milling around our area. The rumor mill was in full swing, as the rest of the battalion settled into our new area of operation. Some were not as likely as others, but all were within reality. One had our guns moving to the battalion hill; another claimed that we would remain where we were; while another had us becoming a roving company. Finally, one rumor even had the entire battalion moving back to our old area again. Scuttlebutt was like the wind—blowing hard one minute and dead calm the next. One didn't know what to believe! Although I learned early on not to believe anything until it happened, one always felt a compelling need to place at least a glimmer of hope into a fortuitous rumor.

Our new orders arrived the morning of the third day and they laid to rest the ever-increasing volumes of our rumored destiny. We were to transfer both guns to the new battalion hill and be reassigned to Mike Company. I for one was not overly thrilled about moving to battalion with all the lifers and having to put up with all of their petty bullshit again; however, when I discovered that the orders further indicated that Corporal Eastman would not be moving with us, I was delighted beyond compare!

"Auf wiedersehen!" I mockingly shouted in the direction of Corporal Eastman, as our fully loaded six-by rolled away from the emtpy gun pits.

"Knock it off!" bantered Vic, as he slapped my arm.

"Aye Aye, sir!" I responded in jest. Everyone laughed.

We were on our way to battalion with all of our worldly possessions loaded aboard. It was a little crowded, but we managed. The six-by slowly wound its way through the area of the hill that was occupied by India Company. We had spent many long and trying months with those guys and had been through thick and thin together. A close bond had developed between us, and that made it difficult leaving them behind. It was quite moving to see the entire company waving and calling out salutations as we drove through.

I spotted Timmy Hall standing in the doorway of his hooch. "Good luck, y'all!" he called out.

"You too! And keep your ass down out there, will ya!"

"No sweat, Ski," he cried.

Soon they were out of sight and, almost as quickly, out of mind.

It wasn't long before we rolled onto the new battalion hill. Cautiously, we made our way along the two-lane dirt road toward the eighty-ones area. The truck made a jarring right hand turn off on the dusty road, passed through an opening in a wall constructed of ammo boxes stacked six feet high, and came to a halt near the FDC bunker on our right. Just past the sandbagged bunker were

143

two empty gun pits situated side by side. To our immediate left were four additional gun pits with dilapidated ammo bunkers that were set in line perpendicular to the main road. Behind them were several large tent-type hooches, some of which still retained their original green color, while others stood in evidence of the aging effects from the ever-constant heat and dust. Those few were sun-bleached and dirty brown. The hooches were exactly like the ones we had at battalion when I had first arrived in country many months before. Directly in front of us was a large area totally void of anything at all. The ground there appeared to have been recently graded by heavy machinery but apparently left unfinished. Beyond that, there was an abrupt drop of approximately forty feet down loose dirt, which lead to another portion of the hill, where a sizable LZ was located. The eighty-ones area in total seemed to be a reasonably spacious compound of almost seventy-five meters square; however, it was certainly in a dismal state of disarray and badly in need of repair!

A few hours after arriving and stowing away our gear, we were divided into small work parties and assigned to clean up the compound. Several crumbling and useless supply bunkers were torn down and the debris piled off to one side. The resulting heap of scrap material only added to an already existing junk pile, which had been stacked against the compound's wall.

Once that task was completed, an amtrack was put at our disposal for the remainder of the day to remove all of the debris. We loaded what seemed like hundreds of dirt-filled ammo boxes into the amtrack with a lot of toil and sweat. The load was then transported to a designated dump on the outskirts of the hill. It took approximately fifteen minutes to fully load the amtrack with debris each time we left for the dump. To our astonishment, the amtrack was emptied of its contents within a matter of three or four minutes, by a raging mob of Vietnamese, hell-bent on finding something usable for themselves.

Young children and elderly adults alike, desperately battled each other for a discarded ammo box or a piece of broken wood. It was a pathetic sight! We sat atop the amtrack and watched in stunned disbelief as they swarmed the debris-laden interior, even before the hydraulic door had been fully lowered.

A rather bizarre incident occurred on one of the trips to the dump. As the door was being lowered, a young boy was knocked to the ground by the frenzied rush of the crowd and became pinned under its sheer weight. For several long seconds, no one reacted, until the reality of the accident was finally recognized. It seemed like a nightmare! Warning shots were hastily fired into the air to clear the mob away from the partially lowered door. When the door was finally able to be raised, the boy was pulled from beneath it. Immediately, a smile of relief erupted across his face as he was helped to his feet. Only by the grace of God did he escape uninjured, for another inch or two and he would have been crushed.

In no time our compound was squared away, but each new day brought another project to be taken care of. We were certainly kept busy and more than welcomed the end of each long and toilsome day, when we could finally relax a little, hit the EM club, and chugalug a few wide mouth beers.

Gone were the drudgeries of the monsoon, but in its place came the harsh and oppressive heat. Day in and day out the unimpeded rays of the sun's glare affected each of us differently. There were those that tanned normally, a few that suffered like boiled lobsters, and others, like myself, whose complexion easily darkened to a rich coppery brown. The appearance of my skin had embrowned so that I often teased Oliver that by the time we rotated I would be as dark as he.

Mid-rats were midnight snacks prepared by the chow hall and distributed to all that were on gun watch or hole watch around the hill each night. They usually consisted of sandwiches wrapped in wax paper and little else. No matter, they were eagerly consumed without prejudice!

One night, the usual supply of mid-rats was delivered to our

gun pit. Four of us were still up shooting the breeze while we sat
around in the gun pit. Having eaten four of the six sandwiches,
Oliver, Vic, and Lou bid their good nights and turned in. Only Al
and I were left with the remaining uneaten sandwiches. It was Al's
watch and mine was rapidly approaching. Only twenty minutes remained, so I stayed to keep him company. Al needed to relieve
himself and asked, "Ski, would you hang in there a few minutes
while I go take a leak?"

"Sure. I'm not going anywhere."

"Thanks. I'll be right back."

It was a quiet night. We had no fire missions up to then, nor
were there any H&I's scheduled that night either. While Al was
gone, I sat alone in the gun pit leaning up against the sandbags that
formed the circle of the pit. I sat there listening to the muffled
voices of someone's conversation in the nearby hooch. In my
peripheral vision, I spotted the two leftover sandwiches that were
lying on top of the sandbags on the opposite side of the gun pit.
When I next looked, a few seconds later, they were gone! I was
puzzled about their disappearance, for I knew that they had been
there only moments before. I got up to investigate and found them
both on the ground outside of the gun pit. As I picked them up, I
deduced that they had slid off the sandbags by themselves. There
wasn't any other obvious explanation. We had been using plastic
sandbags lately and they were notoriously slippery. We all preferred the cloth type—at least they stayed put when piled on top of
each other.

I returned to my spot and sat back down. By the time I did, the
sandwiches were gone again. "What the hell!" I said aloud. Al returned as I was picking up the sandwiches from the same place, for
a second time. "Everything okay?" he asked.

"No! Not quite."

"What do you mean?" he asked with a perplexing look on his
face.

"While you were gone, I was just sitting here and I looked

over and saw that the sandwiches weren't on the sandbags. When I checked around, I found them on the ground outside of the gun pit."

"Yeah, so?"

"So I put them back and sat back down; then, when I looked over, they were gone again. I could fathom them slipping off once, but twice! I know—you don't believe me."

"I didn't say that."

"You didn't have to. I can see it in your face. Well, I'm going to sit right here and watch them this time."

After sitting there quietly for about ten minutes and beginning to feel like a fool, one of the sandwiches began to slowly slide over the edge and disappear from sight. "There! You see what I mean?"

"Goddamn! You're right, Ski!"

"No shit," I said as we crawled on our hands and knees over to the other side of the gun pit. Peering over the sandbags, we discovered a very large rat gnawing away at the wax paper wrapping. It must have sensed our presence and quickly scurried under the ammo bunker several inches away.

"That son of a bitch was stealing our mid-rats," exclaimed Al in a tone of revelation.

The rest of the night was spent in a battle of wits, with me baiting the rat to show itself in the open and it trying to capture a meal without loosing its life. The rat was obviously driven by survival and encouraged by hunger to continually place itself in certain danger. Even with its lower level of intelligence, its instincts had to have recognized my presence.

When the rat emerged from the hole each time, I would savagely fling my bayonet at it. Time after time, the bayonet impaled only the ground and the rat escaped to safety. Frustrated and growing weary, I switched to hurling my steel helmet down on it. That too was unsuccessful. Al finally gave up watching after an hour and turned in, leaving me alone with my growing obsession.

Losing to a rodent, after almost three hours, was downright

demoralizing. In total frustration and desperation, I seriously considered blasting it with my .45 caliber but thought better of the idea and filled in the rat's exit hole with dirt instead. In the morning, I sprinkled rat poison around the hole as extra insurance. That was the last that I ever saw of the rat!

Intriguing and compelling emotional stress made for strange results (i.e., extending in Nam, reenlisting in the Corps, and desertion). Most prevalent among them was the inducement to extend in Nam for a six-month stint. If a man was so inclined, he was rewarded with a thirty-day leave back in the World, or any other place of his choice. In addition, upon his return to Nam, he became eligible for another R&R as well. Reenlistment, on the other hand, was touted by the career officer as an attractive alternative to civilian life. A sizable cash incentive, immediate single grade promotion, and a choice of duty station all baited the hook. The less seldom selected and morally degrading choice, not to mention a serious general court-martial offense, was going over the hill.

Ken was one of those who, in the opinion of myself and a few other close frields, was unduly influenced. In his case by the enticement of being home for Christmas. Woefully, no matter how hard we tried to reason with him, he remained steadfast and comfortable with his decision. He had made up his mind, electing to extend his tour six months in exchange for those enchanting, yet short thirty days.

We worked on him day and night, making every effort to point out the increased risk of returning home in a body bag—a simple law of averages. We argued the fact that only four months remained on his present tour and that if he extended he would be faced with a total of ten months upon his return—a disheartening thought in itself. We were amazed to learn he would even have to re-up a month and a half in the Corps just to do the additional six months. As a last ditch effort, we appealed to his sense of reality, urging him to consider the psychological effect he would more than likely have to endure when his leave was completed. To our great dismay, we learned that our honest concerns fell on deaf ears. Ken made the final commitment by signing the necessary papers the following day and, indeed, would be home for Christmas.

10. Trek to Da Nang

Lima Company's guns were the second section of our mortar platoon to be stationed on the new battalion hill. It was the same section that had been previously stationed at Phu Loc-Six and the one that my gun squad had covered for a few months earlier. Collectively, our two sections gave us a total of four guns on the battalion hill. The remaining two guns were still out with India Company.

Whisky Lima's section leader, Sergeant Pruitt, was new to them just as our section leader was new to us. Sergeant Pruitt had replaced Lima's old section leader just prior to the big move and was still new in country. Sergeant Semcer, on the other hand, who upon our arrival at battalion was assigned as our new section leader, already had been in country a while.

Sergeant Semcer quickly made his mark as being a stickler for rules and regulations—he went strictly by the book. He was a fair-skinned redneck from Alabama who spoke with a high-pitched southern drawl. Sergeant Semcer always kept his hair in a crew cut and had a distinct aversion for northerners.

One morning, not long after our arrival at battalion, I was manning the FDC phones—one of our new duties in lieu of radio watch—when Lieutenant Dayton walked into the FDC bunker to introduce himself to the section leaders. He had been transferred from Hill 65 a month before our big move. I had never expected to run into him again, so it was like a reunion of sorts when he appeared at the door. I greeted him with a brisk handshake and exhorted, "Come on in, Bill! How the hell are ya?" A quick glance at his collar revealed that he was wearing new rank—silver bars. "I see congratulations are in order!"

"Yeah, the orders came through two weeks ago," he said, beaming from ear to ear. "I'm glad to see a familiar face around here. How's Ken and Al doing?"

"They're both fine. They should be over in the hooch some place, if you want to stop over and see them."

At that very moment, Sergeant Semcer came into the room. I was sure he had overheard our conversation. He properly acknowledged the lieutenant, then immediately turned toward me and began to reprimand me for addressing an officer improperly. "PFC, have you lost your senses? Where the hell do you get off addressing an officer by his first name? You—"

"Sergeant, that's enough!" the lieutenant sternly interrupted. "This man is a personal friend of mine and has my permission to call me by my first name."

"Yes, Sir!" Sergeant Semcer blurted with an indignant inflection in his voice. His face instantly flushed as he turned to me once more. "PFC, you're relieved of your watch. You may leave now," he sputtered through clenched teeth. Without a response, I turned toward the lieutenant, nodded in his direction, and left the FDC bunker.

That day, a one-hundred-round prep-fire mission was scheduled for 1200 hours. Within the previous forty-eight hours, S2 had received reports of an inordinate amount of NVA movement northwest of our hill, approximately two clicks out. First and Second Platoons had already moved into position and were poised to sweep the area upon the completion of our prep-firing the area. On this particular mission, two guns were slated to fire, one from our section and the other from Lima Company's section.

Prep-firing was a technique used to pulverize an area prior to troops moving into it. In our case, one gun usually fired fifty rounds or more in what we referred to as the football field effect. The gunner worked the elevation a half turn—up or down—while at the same time the A-gunner worked the traversing—left or right—an equal amount after each round was fired. This in effect evenly dispersed the rounds throughout an area about the size of a football field: hence its name.

For the past day and a half, both squads had been aware of the impending fire mission and had made the appropriate preparations concerning ammo. During that time, an air of rivalry seemed to have risen between our two squads. Their A-gunner, only four months in country, was being praised as the fastest A-gunner in the battalion—a claim so far unsubstantiated. A considerable amount of pretentious boasting had taken place that simply could not go unchallenged by the men of my section. Wagers were placed left and right and soon involved a large portion of our mortar platoon. I placed no bet of my own, but was extremely flattered that a majority of the bets were placed in my favor.

When the time came for the fire mission, vis-á-vis the contest, the tension in the air could have been cut with a bayonet. Both gun pits were situated adjacent to one another, placing me at a slight disadvantage. In relation to our direction of fire, I was to the left of my opponent's gun pit with my back toward him. As a result, he could easily keep me in view as the contest progressed, whereas I could not afford to glance around at him and lose my rhythm.

With only seconds to go before it was noon, I was relaxed and totally confident that I would soon vanquish my counterpart. I stood poised with one round partially inserted into the muzzle and a second clutched in my left hand. The word was given from the FDC, "COMMENCE FIRING!" I gave the first round a sharp downward thrust and heard it fire an instant ahead of my rival's. From that second on, our squad worked at a feverish pace keeping me supplied with rounds as fast as I could drop them.

I kept a mental count of the rounds as I dropped them, but soon lost track of time. I knew I had the edge, having gotten a round off first. Subsequently, I felt as though I was extending my lead. Fifty rounds would have ordinarily taken a relatively short period of time; however, with the need to adjust after each round, the time was increased threefold.

Even though I wore earplugs fashioned out of MPC, the continual sound of the rounds firing only inches away from my ears induced a terrible ringing inside my head. That, coupled with sweat streaming from my forehead into my eyes, and the right side of my hair repeatedly singed with each blast, did not disturb my methodical and machinelike cadence.

Oliver confirmed my running count when he informed me that there were only five rounds left to fire. As I dropped my next to last round, I no longer heard the other gun firing. For a second I doubted my lead, until I turned and discovered that the opposition still had four rounds to fire. Unfortunately, they had developed a hang round in their tube. In any event, they would have lost no matter what.

They were humbled by sheer experience and had to pay dearly for their highfalutin' and brash attitude. I turned toward my vanquished opponent and his squad and with a smug snicker remarked, "*Xin Loi*, man."

The next morning, I found myself assigned to a work detail at the hand of Sergeant Semcer. He stood waiting for me at the entrance to the FDC and called me over as I was on my way to the chow hall, along with several of the others of my squad. "You're to report to the battalion sergeant major immediately after chow," he sneered.

"Okay, Sarge. But why?"

"You're assigned to a special detail. That's why! And bring your helmet, flak jacket, and weapon with you."

I began to seethe inside but retained my cool and deliberately retorted, "Whatever you say, Sarge." I walked away and quickly caught up with the others.

"What was that all about, Ski?" asked Lou.

I shook my head in bewilderment and said, "Nothing. . . . . He's just pissed off that the lieutenant jumped in his shit yesterday, down in the FDC, when he was chewing me out. Now he's getting back at me, that's all."

"Serves him right! That asshole always has the rag on," muttered Lou to no one in particular.

"What happened in the FDC?" asked Vic.

"Fuck it! It's a long story."

The subject was dropped and nothing more was said about it. As we continued to chow, I wondered to myself what kind of detail it would be and the more pissed off I became. "Probably the garbage run or something equally shitty, knowing him," I mumbled under my breath.

Lacking much of an appetite, I finished breakfast long before the others and returned to the hooch. I collected my gear and made my way down the main road to the sergeant major's hooch. There, I found him standing outside talking with two other marines. Out of sheer respect for his rank—not because regulations dictated it—I saluted him and announced, "Reporting as ordered, sir!" Not waiting for a return salute, I dropped mine and stood at ease. He immediately acknowledged my presence and inquired, "What company are you from, marine?"

"H&S Company, eighty-one's, sir."

"Oh, yes," he replied. His reaction puzzled me. I wasn't sure if the inflection in his voice meant that he knew why I was there or that he had simply recognized the unit name. Whichever it was, his facial expression seemed friendly enough.

The typical sergeant major was 110 percent Marine Corps, and ours was no different. He was in his late fifties, about six-foot-three, in excellent physical shape, sported a typical lifer haircut, and wore immaculately clean stateside utilities—the old style—with sergeant major (E-9) insignia pinned to both collars and a third one on his perfectly starched utility cover. His face had the appearence of worn leather, textured with lines of maturity. His voice was booming and guttural. Every aspect of his appearance exuded command. Even officers below the rank of major respectfully addressed him as "sir." Likewise, it would have been a cardinal sin for anyone to address him as merely "Sarge."

Across the road was a six-by parked with its engine noisily knocking and rumbling away. Its driver, as it turned out, was one of the two marines who was standing with the sergeant major. I vaguely recognized him when I first approached the three of them standing there, but didn't know his name. "Okay, men, the three of you will be on your own to scrounge up as much building material as you can muster in Da Nang and be back here with it by tomorrow evening, before the roads close. It's imperative that we have this material to build new bunkers and repair some of the others on the hill," barked the sergeant major. Turning to the driver of the truck, the sergeant major continued, "Corporal, you're in charge. I trust that I can depend on the three of you and that you'll do an excellent job?" Before any one of us could respond, he abruptly walked off, leaving us standing there alone.

Without delay, we crowded into the cab of the truck and were on our way. I learned, from a quick introduction, that the corporal's name was Steve Wallace—he was from the motor pool—and the other member of our trio was John Bunt—a PFC from the battalion armory. Each one of us had by then served more than nine months in country. We were old salts and were eagerly looking forward to a short reprieve from battalion and a little freedom in Da Nang.

Corporal Wallace threw caution to the wind as we hightailed it to Da Nang. The truck sped along the roads at such a speed that it created miniature whirlwinds of dust trailing behind us. I remember thinking, God help us if a water buffalo wandered into our path. The result would have been like hitting a brick wall.

Fortunately for all of us, we made it to Da Nang in one piece.

Once there, the three of us unanimously concurred that a brief stop at Red Beach, before we began our assigned task, was in order. We easily found our way to the rather large R&R center there and thoroughly enjoyed ourselves for a few brief hours. Lounging around in softly padded chairs of the R&R center, while speaking with several of the Red Cross girls, was an absolute delight. But bathing in the refreshingly cool air of the air-conditioned building was a treasured luxury. It was like an entirely different world there, away from the boonies.

Realizing that time was fleeting, and our task at hand was still to be accomplished, John and I began searching everywhere for Corporal Wallace. He had disappeared from sight for more than an hour and was nowhere to be found. When concern turned to worry, Wallace abruptly appeared in the main activity room among scores of others, with a Red Cross girl clinging to his arm. She stared leeringly at him as though she were mesmerized by his every word. "Hey, Ski! Will ya get a load of this shit!" cried John as he directed my attention across the room. "Look! Loverboy wasn't fuckin' lost at all! He's got that little red-head hanging all over him."

"Well, no shit!" I mumbled aloud, a bit surprised. "Hey! Corporal Wallace," I yelled across the room, "what do ya say, man? It's time to move out—let's go!" John and I finally managed to drag him away so that we could get on with our task.

In no time at all, we made our way into Da Nang and were soon down in the area of the harbor. There, we found ample material for our needs. It was almost like a gigantic open warehouse, with material stored everywhere. Of course, anything we collected was without a formal requisition. That left us in a particularly precarious state of ever-constant vigilance for shore patrols and furious quartermasters.

With relative ease, we soon gathered ample scrap lumber found strewn along what appeared to be a deserted dock. Then we moved on to an adjacent dock that was stocked with pile after pile of wooden crates stenciled with the usual shipping code abbvreviations, most of which were indecipherable, unless one knew the jargon of supply. Without opening them, we had no inkling whatsoever of their contents, so we decided to search elsewhere. Most areas were teeming with work parties and some even guarded by SPs. Those we avoided.

Finally, quite by accident, we stumbled upon an area seemingly unprotected and maybe even forgotten, although I strongly doubted it! The area was hidden from direct view by a series of dilapidated buildings at the far end of the harbor. Corporal Wallace had merely driven behind the first building to turn around, when I spotted hundreds of stacks of cloth sandbags. Beyond that, a huge tarp-covered pile protruded well above the sandbags, which beckoned for further investigation.

Losing no time at all, we first loaded the truck with bundles of sandbags, as we kept a sharp lookout, expecting the shore patrol to show up at any second; then we quickly covered our lading with a large tarp that we had brought along for that specific purpose. With that successfully accomplished, we drew back the tarp of the large towering pile and discovered, to our astonishment, hundreds of sheets of half-inch plywood. Hastily, we unloaded the sandbags from the truck, slid off fifteen four-by-eight-foot plywood sheets from the pile, stacked them flat on the bed of the truck, and then reloaded the sandbags again on top. During this entire time, not one vehicle drove by. Not wanting to press our luck too far, we *didied* out of there ASAP.

The feeling of excitation about pulling off a successful supply raid of Da Nang's harbor was soon gripped by a nervous silence as we slowly departed the area as inconspicuously as possible. After practically holding our breath for the entire time, Corporal Wallace jokingly broke our self-imposed silence. "I think we've managed enough stuff for today. What do you guys think?"

"Yeah, but now what?" John clamored.

"Good question!" I interjected. "I guess we find some place to sack out for the night."

"Yup! And I know just the place!" cried Corporal Wallace as he pounded the steering wheel with the palm of his hand.

"Oh, yeah! Where's that?" John asked with considerable reservation in his voice.

"Over at the Seabee's compound!" he blurted out with an air of self-satisfaction. He pointed through the front windshield. "It's right down this road a ways. I know a chief petty officer there. He owes me a favor and now's the time to collect on it. Look! There's the compound now."

The Seabee's seemingly boundless area paralleled the road for nearly a thousand meters and was fenced in with multiple strings of barbed wire, fortified by several coils of concertina. An artistically painted, billboard-sized wooden placard, indicating their unit designation and displaying a colorful bee in a sailor hat, was conspicuously posted at the approach to the main entrance. The bee at least was worth a chuckle.

The steady whine of the truck's engine dropped several octaves as Corporal Wallace downshifted and swung a wide turn into the compound's entrance. It seemed as though no one was minding the store and we passed through unchallenged.

Once inside, we had no idea where to go, so we simply proceeded to a building directly ahead and plainly marked ADMIN OFFICE. Wallace pulled up to the building and parked in front. "Okay, you guys stay here. I'm going to see what I can do about scrounging up some place to sack out for tonight." He climbed out of the cab and slammed the door closed behind him. "Don't go away. I'll be right back!"

"I hope he knows what the fuck he's doing!" John muttered.

"Yeah, well we've been doing pretty damn good so far," I countered.

Within a matter of minutes, Corporal Wallace emerged from the building and double-timed back to the truck with a look on his face like he had just swallowed a canary. "How did you make out?" John inquired as Corporal Wallace bounded behind the wheel.

"No sweat! I checked with the OD and he gave us the okay to bunk in the transit barracks for the night. And I didn't even have to drop my buddy's name."

"Outstanding!" I exclaimed, rubbing my hands together with anticipation.

"Now all we have to do is find the barracks. He said just follow this road all the way to the end and it will be on the left. That should be easy enough."

We did find the barracks just where the OD said it would be. We left the truck with its precious cargo alongside the barracks unguarded and went inside. Immediately upon entering, a cool gentle breeze swept through the barracks from within. To our surprise, we found all the comforts of home, at least more than we were accustomed to. I was struck by the clean and orderly appearance of the freshly made bunks all in a line with mattresses clad in clean linens, blankets, and pillows—a startling change from the norm. One or two of the bunks were the only ones apparently occupied; the rest had the dress appearance of a pending CG's inspection!

Having chosen three adjacent bunks at about midbarracks, we eagerly took advantage of their irresistible, inviting call. My entire body instantly relaxed on the spring-supported mattress, and my head sank deeply into the soft pillow encased in a crisp, sparkling white pillow case. Compared to the usual dirt-encrusted canvass cot, covered with an inflated rubber lady and draped with a sweat-soaked camouflaged poncho liner at best, we were in seventh heaven.

Lying on my back, with my scraggly jungle boots crossed at the ankles, my fingers interlaced behind my head, and my cover tilted over my face, I lazily informed both John and Corporal Wallace not to disturb me until my flight date came in. At that very instant, I was bombarded with a pillow from either flank. "Enough of this for now," heralded Corporal Wallace. "We have to get some chow before we get down to some serious partying tonight! Wait till you see the slop chute these guys have here!" he warned.

"Oh, yeah! Like what?" I asked.

"The EM club is out of sight, man! And the NCO club is even fuckin' better than that!"

"Yeah, well we can only get into the EM club—remember? We're not E-fours," John snapped.

"That's no sweat! I have it all squared away . . . but first we eat."

Dusk began to creep over the sky as we left the transit barracks and headed to chow. The ground in and around the compound was made up of chiefly sand, due to its close proximity to the water. To facilitate the ease of walking in the sand, wooden walkways had been constructed and crisscrossed the off-road areas of the compound. We made our way through the rear areas of the compound searching for the chow hall and soon became lost. With the aid of one of the permanent personnel, we were aimed in the right direction and soon found it.

Unlike the chow hall, we had little difficulty locating the EM club. Laughter drifted our way as we rounded a darkened building and it came into view. I was astonished at what I saw! There in front of us stood the EM club open on three sides, with a poured cement floor, fluorescent lighting, a pool table, a Ping-Pong table, several tables and chairs, a huge wooden bar, and even a bartender! "Wow! Look at this shit!" I cried.

"Holy shit! This is some place!" John remarked.

"I told you guys," crowded Corporal Wallace.

"Yeah, I know . . . but I didn't expect this!" I said, glancing at Corporal Wallace and grinning widely.

"Come on! What are we waiting for?" urged John.

"You guys go ahead. I'm going to look up my buddy and then I'll meet you back here at, say . . . twenty-one hundred!" said Corporal Wallace.

"Okay. We'll see you later," called John as Corporal Wallace turned and disappeared into the darkness.

John and I stepped out of the shadows and into the light of the

EM club. As we made our way to the bar through the maze of empty tables, I was still reeling with surprise that others actually lived this way in Nam. After being inside a moment or two, my eyes gradually began to adjust to the harshness of the lights. Music softly emanated from an expensive-looking reel-to-reel tape deck, which sat unattended on a stack of RC soda cases in the far corner behind the bar. The selection of oldies swiftly put me into a nostalgic mood and mellowed the constant drone of conversation and laughter in the background. Waiting for service, I kept staring at the clock that hung on the otherwise bare paneled wall in front of us. The barkeep was deeply engrossed in a one-sided debate with a patron, while a friendly contest of eight ball was underway at the pool table. And that was only outdone by the heated game of Ping-Pong raging a few steps away.

When our presence was realized, the bartender motioned in our direction and called out, "What can I get you guys?"

"Two beers!" I said, quickly glancing at John to be sure I was correct. Pulling two ice cold cans of Budwiser from an ice chest below the bar, he routinely tapped the top of each can before opening them with a church key.

"I haven't seen you guys around here before," he said, plunking both cans down on the bar in front of us.

"We're bunking over at the transit barracks for the night," John volunteered.

"Who are you guys with?" he continued.

"Three-seven," I answered.

He made a face as though he recognized the unit and then inquisitively asked, "What's your MOS?"

"Mine's mortars and John here is an armorer," I said.

"No shit? I run the EM club—that's my job," he said. I detected a hint of discontentedness in his voice and after a moment's hesitation found out why. "Yeah . . . I run this place all by my lonesome. I never get a fuckin' break! At night I tend bar and during the day I keep the place stocked, order the beer and soda supplies, clean up—the whole nine yards. . . . "

He continued to ramble on and on about his job and how hard he had it. To listen to him you would think he was up to his eyeballs in misery. I couldn't tolerate much more of his pitiful complaining and had to walk away from the bar before I started something I would regret later. "Someone should send his sorry ass out in the boonies for a day or two. *That* will square his shit away!" John snorted.

"You got that right!" I readily agreed.

The club began to fill up rapidly and the swell of chatter soon surpassed the level of the music. The Ping-Pong rally was over and there were no other takers, so John and I tried our hand and played a set. He wasn't half bad; I lost!

The two of us became quite mellow by the time we were supposed to meet Corporal Wallace, and I desperately needed to relieve myself before we went anywhere. Whenever I drank beer I needed to flush it out nearly as fast as I consumed it.

"You guys ready?" asked Corporal Wallace as he appeared at our table right on time.

"Yup! I am," I mumbled.

"Me too!" echoed John.

"So what the fuck are we waiting for? Let's go!" Corporal Wallace led us to a secluded area just outside the EM club. In the shadows he removed his corporal chevrons from both his collars and handed John and I each one to pin to our utility covers. I was a little leery about impersonating a corporal when I actually wasn't, but was easily swayed as my judgment was already considerably impaired.

"All you have to do is act naturally. Nobody will ask for an ID card," he calmly assured us. We climbed two wooden stairs and entered the noisy NCO club through the front door. Unlike the EM club, it was a totally enclosed hooch. Inside the smoke-filled club we found everyone to be having one hell of a good time singing and joking. In the corner was a sailor sitting on a table squeezing out tunes on an accordion while a group huddled around him harmonizing to the music. Everyone else sat at tables or stood around the bar in small groups swapping stories. Besides the usual fare of beer and soda, the NCO club served liquor as well.

Corporal Wallace apparently got around more than I had thought! We weren't there but a few seconds when he was recognized by several of the guys there. After many short introductions, we drank for free for the remainder of the night. It seemed as though every time I looked someone else was buying us a drink.

Two fights broke out during the first hour we were there, but were soon broken up before any serious damage was inflicted. Then everyone went right back to partying as though nothing had occurred. I soon lost track of the time, but was starkly reminded when two armed SPs entered the door with their .45 calibers at port arms and strongly proclaimed that the club would close fifteen minutes from then—at midnight! I remember thinking to myself, Shit! This place must get awfully wild at times to need weapon-drawn SPs at closing time! Soon after, the club began to empty in an orderly fashion. We shook hands with everyone in sight and then the three of us staggered out of the club.

I honestly don't remember walking back to the transit barracks once I hit the fresh air, nor do I recall sacking out on my bunk. Nevertheless, I was lying on mine when someone came running through the barracks shouting for us to get out and into the bunker outside. I had no idea what was happening, although in the background I could hear a siren sounding. Unconcerned, I rolled onto my side and went back to sleep. Again, I was awaken by someone else, this time an officer I think; he was wailing something about Da Nang's air strip being mortared and for our safety we were to get out and into the bunker. "What? Are you shitting me?" John grumbled. "The goddamn air strip is at least three or four clicks away! These candy-ass sailors . . . "

"Fuck this!" I mumbled as I dozed off to sleep again.

In the morning I awoke with a excruciating headache. The top of my head throbbed to the rhythmic beating of my heart and a constant low-level din buzzed in both ears. Every muscle in my body seemed to rebel at the mere contemplation of movement. Even the backs of my eyeballs hurt. *Hungover* was a gross understatement. John and Corporal Wallace were in no better shape than I. They too suffered the inevitable effects of overindulgence. We skipped morning chow without even having to bring up the subject.

As the morning pressed on, my body became more tolerant to physical exertion and my headache gradually lightened its disabling embrace. Near midday we decided to forgo prolonging our welcome and departed for battalion.

The trek back did little to relieve my self-inflicted misery as I had hoped. On the contrary, every rut in the road, even the most minute, transmitted a bone-rattling jolt that only diminished my recovery. I did, however, revel in the fact that what Sergeant Semcer had thought was punitive action when he placed me on this detail, actually turned out to be a respite in disguise—an irony well worth the discomfort.

Upon our return, the sergeant major was more than pleased with the success of our mission, so much so that he personally commended us to our respective COs, much to the chagrin of Sergeant Semcer.

With Christmas approaching in less than a week, we were kept busy during the day with a new project—a two-man shower. Our platoon commander, Gunnery Sergeant Thompson, ordered the construction. "Just something to help with moral!" he said. Of course he appropriated two water heaters so that there would be hot showers, and he made certain there was ample cement available for laying a floor as well. Even before the construction was completed, our shower became the envy of the battalion.

Bob Hope's Christmas show was scheduled to be presented in Da Nang. We were all eager to see it; however, it was decided that we could spare but one man from our mortar platoon to go. Sergeant Semcer's unorthodox selection method left a lot to be desired. Our names were written on a sheet of paper and affixed to the wall in the FDC bunker. With a toss of a dart the impaled name was the lucky nominee. As fortune had it, Steve Lybin, our radio man, was selected.

He was exuberant over the opportunity and left early the next day, only to return by midafternoon. Disturbed by the fact that he only managed to get within five hundred meters of the stage, he chose not to stay. At that distance, over the vast sea of GIs, even binoculars were of little help.

Both Vic and Lou were getting very short. By their calculations they had less than two weeks before rotating back to the World. I still had one hundred and four days to endure. My short-timer's calendar, initiated only a few weeks before, looked hopelessly empty. Filling in one of the one hundred and twenty circles each day made the time seem to drag with agonizing slowness. It was akin to watching grass grow.

The days preceding Christmas were quiet and rather mundane. Having lived in the Northeast my entire life made it seem inappropriate to associate Christmas with anything but cold weather. In essence, Christmas arrived like any other day for us. The chow hall, on the other hand, attempted to provoke a sense of seasonal cheer by serving a traditional yuletide meal, right down to the eggnog. They even went so far as to decorate the serving area with Christmas lights and bombarded our ears with recorded Christmas carols. Although fleeting, for many it aroused the spirit of the day.

A tragic death by friendly fire marred our celebration that night. The all too familiar sound of small arms fire evoked an urgent rush to empty the EM club. We made a mad dash to our respective areas and awaited further orders. They came, but not what we had expected. Our anxieties rapidly transformed into somberness as we learned of the tragic accidental death of a grunt from Mike Company. He had been standing perimeter watch and had apparently wandered into the wire after tripping out on marijuana. His darkened figure was spotted by his buddy in the adjacent bunker and fired upon after orders to halt were ignored several times. His buddy, horrified and devastated, realized the fate of circumstances, after the retrieval of the body revealed it was that of his close friend.

Being absolved of any wrongdoing by no means relinquished the preponderant burden of anguish he would carry with him for the rest of his life. Merry Christmas?

11.   New Year

The first few days of the final year of the sixties era were indicative of the quiet before the storm. Increased suspicion of a renewed offensive by the North was fostered by the rapidly approaching Lunar New Year. To meet this perceived threat, our battalion readied itself by increasing daytime patrols and nighttime ambushes. Ammo supplies were stockpiled, while replacement troops continually filled our ranks. In addition, India Company's gun section was recalled to battalion, bolstering our fire power to an unprecedented level—six guns. Finally, a constant vigilance was kept on the surrounding mountain areas for any unusual activity.

I was deeply saddened as I watched both Vic and Lou hasten to survey their gear and joyfully prepare to leave Nam. Their orders were cut by the company clerk and their flight confirmed. They were scheduled to depart that afternoon for Da Nang. At the last minute, addresses were exchanged and promises of keeping in touch were exacted. We shook hands and warmly embraced one another before they hurried out of the hooch with seabags in hand. A sudden and peculiar feeling of bereavement seized me at that moment and a solitary tear trickled down my cheek. We had become more than friends; we were comrades. I would miss them.

With their departure barely an hour old, I was charged with the responsibility of squad leader. I had no choice but to accept the position dutifully, recognizing it as a meaningful challenge of my ability or lack thereof. Of course the squad leaders were privy to the new TO before it was posted; however, we had no input into the matter, for it had already been decided by the higher echelon. The squads were thoroughly shuffled and I was dealt a combination of seasoned mortar men and unskilled cherries.

Bill Lawrence, a carefree, eighteen-year-old black from Chicago, was the only one I knew personally in my new squad. He had arrived on Hill 65 two days prior to our move and had been assigned to the other squad. After boasting unrealistically about turning in a 9.8 time in the 60-yard dash to anyone who would listen, he was scoffingly dubbed Nine-eight. Now he would be my A-gunner.

Mike MacLaren, whose primary MOS was mortars, was assigned as my new gunner. Although he had roughly eight months in country and already was a gunner, he was labeled as a loner who was both lazy and arrogant. I was forewarned by several about his attitude and realized he would be my first hurdle of command.

The remaining four ammo humpers were just new in country and all had MOSs other than mortars—a blessing in disguise, for I would not need to retrain them as combat mortar men.

After careful consideration, I decided that discretion was the better part of valor and chose to confront MacLaren one on one before meeting with the entire squad. He bunked in the third hooch down from mine, where I found him lying in his rack with his back toward me when I entered. I sat on the edge of a vacant rack adjoining his and inquired, "Mike MacLaren?"

He quickly rolled over and sat up on the edge of his rack. He was clad in camouflage utility trousers, a gray T-shirt, and dirty brown moccasins with no socks. He stared at me for a second, then softly answered, "Yeah . . . " After a slight pause, I extended my hand and introduced myself.

"Nice to meet you. I hear you're a pretty good gunner, huh?"

"Yeah, not too bad considering," he said smiling, slightly embarrassed at his apparent ability.

"Well, I wanted to meet you before I called the entire squad together. By the way, we're going to be using the first gun pit down on the end, nearest the road. If you want you can move into my hooch down at the end, too. It's closer and there's a few empty racks."

"No, I think I'll stay here, at least for the time being anyway," he said without hesitation.

"No sweat," I said, not wanting to create unnecessary antagonism. I stood up, shook hands with Mike and started for the doorway. Before leaving, I called back, "Nineteen hundred hours at the gun pit. . . . I'll see you there." I felt happy and a bit relieved that it went well. He seemed friendly enough and I felt we should work well together despite his previous reputation.

The word was passed along to the men assigned to my squad about the impending meeting. At 1900 hours we all gathered in the gun pit. I felt a little nervous, although I was not unaccustomed to a position of authority; it was the first such responsibility I had for men in combat. I began by reiterating the squad assignments, "Okay . . . as you all know, or should know, our gun squad and Harvey's gun squad are attached to Mike Company, so if they go . . . so do we! Mike MacLaren's our gunner; Nine-eight is the A-gunner; Dave Sutton is the first ammo humper; Larry Chesney is the second ammo humper; Greg Ewen is the third ammo humper; and Paul Brantly, last but not least, is the fourth ammo humper. Any questions on assignments? Okay. I want you all to understand that if you guys work for me, I'll work for you. I see no reason why we can't become a tight squad and the best in battalion. Also, for the sake of you new guys, we clean the gun each morning and run gun drill each night after chow. Mike and Nine-eight will break you guys in on all the basics: your jobs, the gun, types of ammo, the FDC, how things run around here, and anything else you may need to know. But keep in mind that if you don't ask questions, no one's going to tell you anything. Now . . . there's only two rules

I want enforced: one . . . know your job and do it correctly, and two . . . no smoking in the gun pit. One more thing. If we get hit, you new guys make sure you get your asses out here in the gun pit. Don't go taking off some place on me." I paused, taking a long piercing look at each of the new guys. "If there's no questions then that's it, gentlemen. Welcome aboard!"

For the next few weeks the new guys worked diligently at mastering the nomenclature of the gun, its operation, the intricacies of a fire mission, the hierarchy of command, and the mundane procedure of breaking out ammo. They were a decent bunch of guys, friendly and both eager to learn and to do well. Their inexperience and obvious naive attitudes were as conspicuous as their brand-new jungle utilities and pallid complexions. A condition that only time and knowledge would rectify. Consequently, they received a profusion of banter and the usual demeaning remarks about cherries, but more often than not, they were the unsuspecting recipients of antagonistic pranks. Although it was nothing more than any one of us had to endure when we were cherry, I kept an eye on them anyway, allowing them to fend for themselves and intervening only when it became absolutely necessary.

Likewise, Nine-eight endured the constantly critical eye of his squad leader and mentor. He had an extremely difficult time correcting his tendency of ducking away from the muzzle after dropping each round. In his case it stemmed from his fear of the loud blast and subsequent singeing flash.

Late one afternoon, our gun received a fire mission. A daytime patrol from Mike Company was pinned down in an ambush and frantically called for fire support. Under the circumstances, they requested three rounds of HE instead of a single round of WP to correct on. When Mike had the gun up, Nine-eight resorted to his old habit of ducking after each round. Annoyed at how easily he reverted to force of habit, I ordered him to man the phone during a pause for a correction and I assumed his position as A-gunner to demonstrate the correct technique.

The corrections were repeated to Mike via Nine-eight, and three more rounds were readied by the ammo humpers. Before Mike had the gun up, I stood poised with one round partially inserted in the muzzle and a second clenched in my left hand. The instant he indicated that the gun was up I released my grip on the first round. Without moving my body from the position it was in, I brought the second round to the muzzle in a continuous motion. As I started to insert it, the first round was just then firing. The edge of the fin assembly of the round I was holding in my hand was struck by the exciting round, forcibly spinning me off balance to my right. At the same instant I winced in excruciating pain as a piercing blast bombarded my left ear—the one then facing the tube. I quickly recovered enough to fire the remaining two rounds.

In my haste to correct Nine-eight I neglected to utilize ear plugs. I became so accustomed to not using them as squad leader. Instead, I would place my fingers in my ears when the gun was fired. It was much more convenient that way. Moreover, I failed to realize that our recently surveyed tube would be considerably slower than our old tube, thus causing the near catastrophe. The worn inner diameter of our old tube allowed the round to strike the firing pin a fraction of a second sooner than the tighter fitting new one. Had the second round been inserted, even slightly, the results would have been a grave tragedy, for the entire squad would have surely been killed or wounded.

It wasn't until sometime later, while I was alone with my thoughts, that the affects of what could have possibly happened settled in. When it did, I began to tremble uncontrollably. I couldn't help but conjure up a mental picture of the earlier calamity. I had only myself to blame for my stupidity.

That night, the continual ringing sensation I experienced in my ears began to worry me. I was urged to have them checked at the battalion aid station, but I was reluctant to do so, for fear of the worst—that I may have punctured an ear drum. With the passing days, the ringing subsided and the hearing in my left ear returned to normal.

Two days later (16 January 1969) I was promoted to Lance Corporal, effective retroactive from the first day of January. I was both delighted and proud. Up until then I never wore my PFC rank insignia, but after the promotion I quickly borrowed a Lance Corporal chevron to wear on my utility cover.

The gook shop, which was allowed to operate on the battalion hill, was much larger than we had been accustomed to. Offered for sale was the usual selection of sundry goods and services. Also included were three barbers and a custom-made suit outlet from Hong Kong. A smooth talking salesman did a booming business offering tailor-made suits at reasonably low prices. A wide selection of materials and styles were offered. Stacks of swatch books displaying a multitude of fabrics and colors were available for the customer's perusal. As an enticement for each suit purchased, a monogrammed silk shirt was thrown in as a bonus. I was no less susceptible than the next guy and ordered a medium gray sharkskin, double-breasted suit with continental-style trousers. In addition to the bonus custom-made silk shirt, I ordered two more as well. Two separate delivery options were offered: delivery to me within five weeks, or at a slight additional cost it could be shipped home to coincide with when I rotated. I chose to have it sent home, reasoning that it would more than likely mildew in my seabag before I rotated.

The battalion sergeant major paid frequent surprise visits to the Vietnamese-operated barber shop. He would make every effort to pester the barbers to give GI haircuts and intimidate the men to get them. After removing his cover and stroking his naked gourd, he invariably exacted a verbal commitment from each man before he departed. Although upon his departure most reneged, the new guys feared the wrath of a reprisal and meekly acquiesced.

The sergeant major's apparent lack of influence on both the barbers and the men clearly made him rethink his strategy. Not long after, he cleverly conceived the notion of offering free haircuts to the men, enlisting a budding tonsorial artist from within the ranks of the battalion. (Curiously enough, no one was sure in what fashion this guy was compensated.) He even went so far as to requisition a prefabricated hooch, which was flat-bedded in and located opposite our area. The only qualifying hitch was that the person utilizing his free service had to comply with the only steadfast style offered—the sergeant major's special! Even so, the barber was seldom idle.

Fifty-five gallon drums filled with water and situated next to each gun pit were the only means of extinguishing a fire if one were accidentally started, so when the squad leaders were asked if there was anything we might need to requisition from supply, dry chemical fire extinguishers were requested. To our surprise, the request was quickly acted upon and the extinguishers were provided.

No sooner had ours been mounted to the blast wall located between the ammo bunker and the gun pit itself, then did I have the occasion to utilize it. I had just entered our hooch and observed the flimsy electrical wiring, which was loosely strung from support pole to support pole, aflame. Even though the light bulb was still lit, the fire slowly spread along the wire. Startled, I shouted, "FIRE!" and pointed toward the burning wire above Harvey's bunk. With that I dashed back to the gun pit, only a few steps away, and returned with our spanking-new fire extinguisher in hand. With perfect aim, I doused the flames with the white powdery chemical. It dispatched the fire almost immediately. Consequently, Harvey and his bunk were beneath my line of fire and were literally covered with a coat of falling residue.

"What the fuck are you doing?" shouted Harvey as he stood there covered in white. "Look what you've done to my rack!"

"*Xin Loi,* man. I was only putting out the goddamn fire. What was I supposed to do? . . . let the fuckin' hooch burn down?"

"You could have at least aimed in a different direction so that this shit wouldn't have landed on all my stuff. Look at me! I'm all white, and I just took a shower, too! Shit!" he shouted, trying to brush away the white chalky powder.

Once the danger had passed, it struck me as quite amusing to see Harvey clad in only a towel and coated from head to toe in white. The more annoyed he became, the more hysterical his predicament seemed. When I was finally able to stop laughing, I did my best to help Harvey clean up his area. It was the least I could do. (Our fire extinguisher was never replaced.)

Steve Lybin returned from his R&R the next day chomping at the bit with the news that he had gotten engaged while in Guam! "You did what?" asked Oliver, astounded over Lybin's revelation.

"Yeah, before I left I bought Felicia a diamond ring. She's going to wait for me to come back. Then we're going to get married," he related with all sincerity.

"Time out a minute! Let me get this straight. You're telling us that you met this girl on R&R, who you don't know from Adam, except for the few days you were there, and you bought her a diamond ring? You really expect that she's going to wait for you to come back and marry her?" I asked sarcastically.

"Yes!" he answered adamantly.

"Man, you are *dinky dow* in the head! You got your first piece of ass and you think you're in love. Ten to one she's a prostitute and probably had that ring hocked the second you boarded the plane. That broad gave you a line of shit, man! She's probably telling everyone right now about that easy American marine she fucked—in more ways than one!" Oliver bluntly stated.

"No way, man! She's in love with me. I know it. And I'm going back to marry her, one way or another," Lybin shouted defensively.

"You're fuckin' *dinky dow!* Just how the hell do you think you're going to manage to get back there? You have two and a half years left to do in the Corps!" I pointed out.

"I'm going to request duty there when my tour is over—that's how!"

"The Corps doesn't have a duty station in Guam!" I countered.

"I know, but they have an embassy there. I gave it a lot of thought on the way back on the plane. If I re-up in the Corps for two more years, I get my choice of schools and I'll request embassy school."

"Well, you better go talk to the career officer, because it just doesn't happen that way. Only the top 10 percent get chosen for embassy duty, and only the top one or two out of those get their choice of duty stations. Then there has to be an opening at the one you want! Do you know what the odds are of that happening? You'll probably have a better chance making commandant of the Marine Corps!" I brusquely told him.

"Yeah, well, I'm going to fuckin' do it if it's the last thing I do!" he cried. Lybin became visibly upset before storming out of the hooch.

"We better back off a little, Ski. He might do something fuckin' stupid," observed Oliver.

"I think you're right. Maybe we should have a talk with the chaplain. Maybe *he* can talk some sense in to him," I suggested.

After reluctantly seeking counseling with the chaplain and writing her countless letters that went unanswered, Lybin sadly realized he had been duped.

Gunny Thompson decided to put together a barbecue for eighty-ones as another one of his morale boosters. He persuaded the mess sergeant—a good friend of his—to supply the necessary food. Then he scrounged up a few makeshift grills made from cut-down fifty-five gallon drums. I don't know how he squared it with the battalion CO, but he did that too.

The morning of the barbecue we checked off the radio net for an entire twenty-four-hour period—an unprecedented action. Early that day, we squared away the area and prepared ourselves for what basically amounted to a day off. The barbecue began rather slowly, but soon gained momentum. Although the shindig was meant for us, as the day progressed, a good percentage of the battalion personnel dropped in at one time or another. Of course, there were some who came and then failed to leave; however, they were among the minority. Even the colonel made an unexpected appearance and stayed for a few beers.

Soda and beer were plentiful and flowed freely from the stockpile the gunny had managed to obtain. A friendly game of touch football—unrefereed—escalated into a rough and tumble bout of tackle ending in a near fisticuff. A milder form of entertainment pitted myself and Brunnell against the gunny and a lieutenant from Special Services in a contest of pitching horseshoes. The odds were stacked in our favor, for Brunnell was practically reared on the game back home. We easily defeated all challengers, until we could barely lift another shoe, no less toss one.

By early evening, the food and drink were totally depleted. Most everyone had gone, except those diehards too drunk to realize that their welcome was overextended. They were readily corralled and quietly escorted on their way. Shortly after, we all gathered around the gun pit. In appreciation, a rousing chorus of "He's a Jolly Good Fellow" spontaneously hailed our platoon commander, Gunnery Sergeant Thompson. No matter who you asked in our mortar platoon, the consensus was the same. The gunny was by no means the typical lifer.

That night, the partying continued on a less ostentatious scale. Personal supplies of warm beer, an occasional bottle of VO or Gordon's gin, and a handful of Darvons were broken out. We sat around in our respective hooches in small groups here and there, playing cards and shooting the breeze, while others wandered from hooch to hooch.

As time crept on, I became totally wasted by the cumulative effects of the countless beers of the day and the gin that I drank that night. All of that was topped off by the synergistic effect of the single Darvon capsule I had popped as well. Suddenly, the entire world around me appeared to move in slow motion as the effects took hold. I vaguely recall sitting on my rack thumbing through a magazine. Sounds and conversations around me were combined together in a dull roar, sounding much like a phonograph record played at an abnormally slow speed. Although I could plainly see myself turning the pages of the magazine, there wasn't the slightest sensation of movement.

Within minutes, I became extremely somnolent and had a sudden desire to lie down. No matter how hard I tried, though, my body refused to respond. Harvey sat opposite me in silence, devilishly grinning from ear to ear and looking more and more ominous as I stared back at him in bewildering frustration. I implored him to stop grinning at me, then begged him in the same breath to help me lie down on my rack. As I did, I saw his mouth move in a snail-like pace in response to my request and helplessly watched as he eased me over on my side.

Time was so warped that I had no reference with which to gauge its passing. What seemed like an eternity was probably no more than a quarter of an hour or so. A deluded feeling of circular motion commenced as my eyes focused on the ceiling of the tent. As though it would help, I desperately tried to stop the ever-increasing and nauseating sensation by dangling my leg over the side of my rack. Sensing that the inevitable was rapidly approaching, I struggled to roll out of my rack and staggered in a stupor to the shower stall. There I stood, fully dressed in my utilities and jungle boots, dousing myself with water. Thankfully, the spinning and nausea diminished somewhat by the sudden invigoration of cold water.

Sopping wet, I stumbled back to the hooch and fell on my rack face first. Within seconds, the horrible queasiness resumed worse than before the shower. A rancid taste of bile rose in my throat and I began to gag uncontrollably. With one hand cupped over my mouth and the other clenching my stomach, I scrambled to get out of the hooch. Once outside, I barely made it to the rear of the hooch before I began to puke on the ground repeatedly. To my relief, the nausea was gone and I was finally able to fall asleep.

Several days later, just after midnight, we were awakened by the sound of sustained small arms and machine gun fire. In no time at all the duty gun was manned and immediately instructed to fire a single round of illumination. It was soon followed by an HE fire mission directed toward the west side of the hill.

Suddenly, more firing erupted as men scrambled in the shadows to take up their positions. As a natural reaction, my squad, as well as the others, dashed to our respective gun pits, donned helmets and flak jackets, and waited.

Soon, a familiar voice from the FDC came over the gun pit phone and directed my gun to fire solely illumination rounds. With the phone pressed tightly to my left ear and my finger inserted in the other, I listened closely as Sergeant Semcer's voice came on the line a second later and called, "Gun one?"

"Gun one!" I shouted back.

"Stand by for a fire mission!" he said plainly. Pausing only a second, he issued the coordinates. "Nine o'clock. Deflection: four—eight—seven—fiver. Elevation: one—one—two—zero. One round illumination. Time setting: fifteen seconds, charge two. Fire when up!" I repeated the coordinates to my squad as I was given them and they immediately readied the gun to fire. Within seconds, the gun was up and Nine-eight nervously called out, "Stand by!" as he dropped the first round.

As we waited to fire again, my adrenaline flow increased dramatically by the surrounding stimuli. The other guns began firing intermittently and added to the din of the already raging battle engulfing our hill. An occasional hand flare was popped by those in bunkers at various locations around the perimeter to assist in providing localized luminosity.

In the flickering light of our powerful illumination rounds, drifting clouds of dense grayish smoke were highlighted in an eerie golden-orange tinge. At the same time, an overpowering smell of cordite hung thick in the air around our gun pits.

Soon after, a correction in elevation was ordered to compensate for the wind, and we fired another illumination round. This time it popped further out and slowly drifted back over the intended area. A voice came over the phone. "Gun one!" It was Sergeant Semcer again.

"One!"

"Continue to fire one round of illum every forty-five seconds with the same charge and coordinates, unless I tell you differently!" he quickly ordered.

"Okay," I replied. I glanced in the direction of the four new guys standing between Nine-eight and the ammo bunker and recognized the look of tense confusion on their faces. It was the first time since they had arrived in country that they had experienced an actual combat situation. They seemed a little shaken, but that was expected.

"You guys okay?"I asked. They did little more than nod affirmatively. At that same instant, the gun next to our's fired two rounds of HE. I watched in amusement as the four of them instinctively crouched in unison.

"Just try and forget what's going on around you and concentrate on your jobs," I said calmly in the lull. "Break out twenty rounds of illum and set them for fifteen seconds, charge two." The noise level had risen I was talking and I had to shout in order to be heard. "Then give me a count of the total illumination we have left. Okay?"

"Twenty-eight rounds, including the one Nine-eight is holding," Brantly called out a few seconds later.

"Okay. Open any canisters that aren't already and stand by," I sharply instructed.

I kept a close watch on the illumination situation high above us, estimating when each subsequent round should be fired. I made certain that there were at least two rounds lit at all times.

As the spent illumination parachutes floated on the wind, they drifted aimlessly, leaving a trail across the shadowy canopy of the night sky. They were scantily illuminated by the scintillating glare of the subsequent rounds. Their presence added to the eeriness of the night.

Fire missions continued to be fired by the others' guns as

well, although they fired less frequently than we did. Consequently, we were soon down to five rounds. I dutifully informed the FDC of our shortage of illumination. With no immediate cessation in sight, I was instructed to utilize the illumination rounds from the other guns as necessary.

I pointed to Harvey's gun pit and ordered, "Chesney, Ewen, and Brantly—get whatever illumination rounds they have on the next gun and make it ASAP!"

I looked up and saw that it was time to fire the next round. "Okay, Nine-eight, fire." My instruction went unheard. "NINE-EIGHT!" I shouted. He was staring at the sky and quickly turned toward me with a wide-eyed startled look. "Fire the fuckin' round!" I demanded. He finally complied.

After an extended lull, the pace of firing rapidly resumed as renewed fire fights ensued. Again, I ordered illumination rounds to be collected, but this time from all the remaining guns. "FDC, this is gun one," I called into the phone. No one answered. "FDC, are you there?"

"This is FDC. What's the matter?" a voice answered in an annoyed tone.

"This is gun one. We are extremely low on illum. We have only twelve rounds left," I informed the unfamiliar voice.

"Okay, wait one!" the voice said.

A second later, Sergeant Semcer came on. "What the hell did I tell you? Use the rounds from the other guns and keep the goddamn area lit up out there!" he admonished.

"But—"

"No buts. I don't have time for your shit. Just do it. That's an order!"

"Why you son of a bitch," I muttered under my breath. "I'll fix you, you dumb confederate shit!"

"What did he say?" asked Mike.

"He wouldn't listen to me, so we'll just have to fire till there's no more," I answered.

"Then what?" asked Nine-eight.

"Your guess is as good as mine!"

Things began to quiet down for the last time, and we soon fired the only remaining illumination round. Then, several minutes later, darkness reclaimed the night. Only the cooling amber glow of the last spent illumination round could still be seen swaying gently to the ground beneath its parachute. Almost five minutes passed before our FDC was made aware of the lack of illumination in the sky. Sergeant Semcer suddenly snarled over the phone, "Gun one! Why the hell aren't you firing?"

Very calmly, I smugly replied, "Because we don't have any left, Sarge."

"You shitbird! I told you to use the rounds from the other guns, you incompetent asshole!" he barked.

"We did! And we fired them all, too."

"What? Then why the hell didn't you advise me when you were getting low?" he shouted, spitting mad.

"I did, when we were down to twelve rounds. That's when you told me that you didn't have time for my shit, remember?" I retorted.

"You smart ass. Report to me at the FDC immediately!" he ordered.

"Yes, sir!" I answered sarcastically.

When I arrived inside the busy FDC, Sergeant Semcer was so infuriated that his eyes were flashing fire and he stammered as he read me the riot act. He continued to indecorously berate me in front of all present. It was a very demeaning experience, especially since I was being wrongly traduced. At one point, I feared he was going to strike me and I took a step backward in passive defense. During Sergeant Semcer's endless rambling, I tried repeatedly to explain what had actually transpired, but I was not allowed. Prior to dismissing me, Sergeant Semcer swore that I would receive office hours for what he claimed was my insubordinate conduct.

Fortunately for me, Gunny Thompson was well aware of my

integrity and dependability. After reviewing Sergeant Semcer's spitefully aspersive allegations and interviewing me about what had transpired, Gunny Thompson concluded that there was an insufficient basis for me to receive office hours. In fact, I later learned through the grapevine that Sergeant Semcer was told in no uncertain terms to back off and to cease harassing me.

From the previous night's activity, our total ammo count had become dangerously low. Consequently, a resupply was urgently requested.

The following day, a tractor-trailer arrived laden with pallets of ammo. It carried more than I had ever seen in one place at any given time, other than in an ammo dump. Not only was ammo ordered to replenish our exhausted supply, but also an additional amount was ordered. A work party consisting of our entire mortar platoon worked furiously throughout the day to break open and stack ammo for our gun pit ammo bunkers. Our area was clogged with metal packing straps, empty wooden pallets, opened ammo boxes, and dozens of piles of unopened canisters strewn everywhere. By the end of the day, we were exhausted and deservingly ready to relax and down a few beers.

One afternoon, upon returning from chow, I heard a familiar voice coming from within our hooch as I approached. Inside the doorway stood Ken beaming from ear to ear. He had just returned on the admin run. "Hey, look who's back! I thought it was your voice that I heard," I called out, happy to see him again.

"Ski! Good to see ya! How've you been? Where's everybody else? At chow?" he asked cheerfully.

"I'm fine. And yes, the others are at chow. The question is how have you been? Everything okay back in the World?" I inquired.

"Everything's great! It was outstanding!" he said excitedly.

"How's Bonnie? Was she happy to see you?" I asked.

"Of course, are you kidding! But I'll tell you, I had one hell of a time with her when it came time to come back. She didn't want me to leave for shit. She was really upset the night before," he recalled.

"Yeah, I bet. It must have been nice spending Christmas with your family, though." I speculated.

"It sure was, but in a way I missed being here with you guys," he admitted.

"Yeah, well I'm glad to see you back," I told him.

Just then the others returned and the questions began again. That night we had a little celebration to welcome Ken back.

Two days later, a close friend of Ken's, who had also extended his tour in Nam, returned that morning. He stopped at our hooch to visit while his squad was out on a patrol. A short time later, that same patrol was engaged in a fire fight and became pinned down in an ambush. The remainder of his platoon scrambled off the hill to their aid. Driven by loyalty, he volunteered to go out with them, even though he didn't have to.

Although I didn't know him very well, I too mourned his untimely death when we sadly learned that he had been killed attempting to rescue a wounded buddy. All but one of his squad had been wiped out in the ambush.

The next day we learned of the gruesome details. It was explained to us that he had heroically crawled out to a badly wounded fellow marine, who was moaning in agony, fully aware of the possible consequences. The gooks held their fire until he reached his mortally wounded buddy; then, with extreme prejudice, he was deviously met with a deadly hail of machine gun fire. It was not until his platoon received support fire from our guns that they were able to safely retrieve their lifeless, bullet-ridden bodies.

His brave and unselfish actions were surely worthy of the Silver Star. But be that as it may, it was shamefully ironic that he was dealt such a cruel fate on his first day back in Nam.

12.   R&R

After ten and a half months in country, I decided to recant my earlier decision to forgo R&R in lieu of saving for my car. Precious
little ever remains status quo, ergo, no longer did acting frugal
seem to hold as much meaning as it had when I was still new in
country. I reasoned that it was more important that I go on R&R,
no matter where it was, than to endure chastity any longer. I suppose all those delightfully sordid stories, brought back from R&R
by those who had gone before me, were much too alluring for me
not to experience for myself.

Having made up my mind to take my R&R, I informed
Sergeant Semcer of my decision and requested the next available
R&R slot. Since I had elected not to take my turn previously, I
now had preference due to my seniority. As it happened, three
slots for Hong Kong were allotted to our mortar platoon in the
upcoming weeks. Of the three, I chose the second slot in mid-Feb-
ruary. Coincidentally, Oliver was scheduled to go to Hong Kong
ten days before me and Harvey four days after me.

Since my decision was made on such short notice, I needed to
borrow some additional money. I had only $213; $250 was the
minimum required in order to go on R&R. Luckily, Ken felt
generous and lent me $100. With a total of $313 in my pocket,
I felt that I was set to enjoy myself on R&R for five whole days.

As the time drew closer, the days began to drag at an unbearable pace. It became increasingly difficult to contain my excitement about going to Hong Kong. It was all I could think about. Then the day finally came for Oliver to leave, and I knew that I would soon follow.

When Oliver returned the next week, he was filled with stories of pleasurable delights. He rambled on about where to go, what to see, and what there was to do. He made specific mention about a bar called Whisky-A-Go-Go, the Presidential Hotel's discotheque and restaurant, and dwelled upon a blue-eyed, blond-haired oriental call girl who commanded fifty dollars a night. He quickly qualified himself in that she was outstanding, but, nonetheless, most definitely out of his price range.

In preparation, I first retrieved my seabag from storage and removed from it my only two civilian shirts, one pair of civilian trousers, and, of course, my dress uniform shoes. Then I carefully packed my ditty bag with my civvies and two walking suits that I had wangled from one of my buddies.

The next morning I was off on the morning admin run to Da Nang. Before I left, I bid my squad farewell as they began the task of dismantling our ammo bunker and rebulding it—a project I was glad I wouldn't be around for.

When I arrived at the R&R center in Da Nang, I checked in and immediately began processing through. There were several long lines, the first of which was to check and validate travel orders. As the line moved forward, I caught a glimpse of the officer sitting behind the table and suddenly bacame panic-stricken. He was the very same major with whom I had a run in with several months earlier when Ken and I were in Da Nang. The two of us were walking along as the major approached from the opposite direction. I had a case of soda tucked under one arm and a cigarette in my right hand. When he came to within saluting distance, Ken did and I did not. Whether he noticed my cigarette or not I wasn't sure, but he stopped and chewed me out for not saluting. To add fuel to the fire, I told him that I couldn't have very well saluted with a cigarette in my hand and went on to curtly inform him that in the bush officers weren't saluted. Well, needless to say, that didn't go over very well. He became infuriated and proceeded to castigate me in front of Ken. Now I was praying he wouldn't remember me, or I would be in a world of shit, for it was his approval that would allow me to go on R&R.

When it was my turn, I adhered strictly to correct military bearing, held my breath, and crossed my fingers. He scribbled his signature on my orders without even looking up from the table. I had skated through, thank God! Then it was on the next line to have my shot card checked. It was up to date and therefore I didn't need shots. I skated there also. Next it was on to the disbursing line. I changed my MPC back into greenbacks and it was verified that I had the minimum amount necessary to go on R&R. Finally, I was assigned a flight number and a departure time.

Out on the flight line, a large group of us anxiously milled around anticipating a week of sorely needed R&R. The designated flight time came and went and we were still on the flight line. We patiently waited, and waited, and waited in the sweltering afternoon sun. Finally, the plane arrived four hours late. We boarded the commercial airliner and promptly took off for Hong Kong.

The plane made its final approach, landing in Hong Kong at approximately 2300 hours. Once off the plane, we were directed into a customs area where we were subjected to a complete and thorough search of our meager luggage and of our person. We were told they were checking for illicit drugs. At the time it seemed little more than an unnecessary annoyance, in fact it was quite preposterous. The availability of drugs in Hong Kong surely surpassed any amount that may have been smuggled in.

With the formalities completed, we were taken to the R&R center. There we were subjected to a brief indoctrination, warned about off-limit areas, selected hotel accommodations, and converted our greenbacks into Hong Kong dollars. The rate of exchange was unreal—one Hong Kong dollar to 13 cents American money! I converted $250 and ended up with a huge wad of money in large denominations. Then we were given a list of hotels and requested to choose our first, second, and third choices. Selections were based on seniority; officers first. By the time they got down to me, I feared there would be little left to choose from. To my surprise, I was able to get a room in the hotel of my second choice— the Grand Hotel. With all the incidentals out of the way, we eagerly boarded a shuttle bus and were transported to our respective hotels.

It was just after midnight by the time I checked in at the main desk and got settled in my room. Still dressed in my utilities, I stood in the center of the room and gaped at all the luxuries that it had to offer. Unlike the sparse accommodations that I had been accustomed to for the past ten and a half months, it was clean, dry, and luxurious. My room contained its own bathroom with hot running water, electric lights, a phone, heat and AC, two double beds, night tables, a triple dresser with a mirror, wall-to-wall carpeting, and a large picture window. In comparison to the paltry conditions I was used to, I felt like royalty.

Wasting no time I stripped off my utilities and lavished myself with a hot and lengthy shower, ridding my body of layers of ground-in dirt. Taking as long as I pleased, I savored the pleasure of showering in a real bathroom! After my shower, I stood barefooted on the cool tile floor, in front of the mirror, wrapped in a clean white bath towel, and treated myself to a shave in a sink that had hot running water. It felt sensational! I could hardly believe it was happening. How quickly one forgets the simple amenities that so many take for granted back home.

Eager to check out the action, I donned my civvies, stuffed my bank roll into my back pocket, collected my room key and cigarettes, and was off for the hotel lounge. As I slammed the heavy door to my room behind me and began to walk down the narrow carpeted hall toward the elevator, I felt alarmingly naked without a weapon and extremely cautious. While waiting for the elevator and then during the ride down to the main lobby, I consoled my fears and soon was able to render them free of any further concern.

With little difficulty, I found my way to the lounge on the lower level. In the cramped smoke-filled room, a middle-aged oriental male, dressed in a red waistcoat with matching bow tie, busied himself with typical bartender chores. At the center of the nearly empty room was a small round table occupied by a couple engaged in what seemed to be an endearing conversation. In the far mirrored corner of the room, a male piano player laggardly accompanied a female vocalist. She was British or Canadian, definitely not oriental as I would have suspected. At the bar itself sat two Americans downing glass after glass of beer, totally oblivious to what was happening around them.

I knew the minute I entered the lounge that it was not where the action was; however, feeling committed to at least having one drink before departing, I selected a stool at the bar where I could easily view the entertainment. The bartender was extremely polite and returned in no time with my Tom Collins drink. I emptied the puny glass in a few swallows and nursed the remaining ice right through the singer's next song, then I hastily made my exit.

Once outside, I decided to play it by ear and walked a little. I soon discovered that even at that time of the night things were bustling almost everywhere. As I rounded the corner, down the street from my hotel, I was verbally accosted by an obvious employee of a local bar. In Pidgin English, he ran down an entire gamut of reasons why I should spend my time and money there. Being overly suspicious of orientals, I informed him that when I was good and ready I would patronize his bar and continued to walk along. Spotting a taxi across the street, I flagged it down. Persistently, he continued his spiel as he followed me to the cab jabbering the entire way. As I climbed into the back of the cab, he flicked out a business card from his shirt pocket espousing the bar and its services; then thrusting it through the open window he said,

"You don't find what you want, you come back here, okay?"

Annoyed at his unyielding persistence, I snatched the card from his hand and angrily instructed the taxi driver to take me to the Whisky-A-Go-Go bar. The driver turned toward me and rattled off something in Chinese that I didn't understand. When I repeated my request, he addressed the man who had handed me his business card and who was still standing by the cab. They quickly exchanged a few words and looked at me with a puzzled frown. Realizing that they were feigning ignorance I shouted, "Never mind! Take me to the Presidential Hotel."

The driver nodded in compliance, threw the cab in gear and was off in an instant. Subsequently, I got the ride of my life as we sped along on the opposite side of the street, zigzagging in and out of traffic. Hong Kong had no speed limit; consequently, everyone drove like maniacs.

Minutes later, I arrived at the Presidential Hotel safe, but a tad shaky. Inside, the discotheque was alive with music, dancing, and servicemen having a wild time. Instantly, I realized that Oliver neglected to tell me that it was a place to bring an escort, not to find one! I was rapidly becoming frustrated over wasting the night away; then I remembered the business card and the guy's assurance of finding what it was that I was looking for.

I hailed the first cab that came long, jumped inside and handed the driver the business card. "Take me here!" I said, somewhat annoyed with myself. Without a word we sped off to my chosen destination. This time, I was not bothered by the ride, for I was too busy grumbling to myself about arriving here late and the prospects of spending my first night in Hong Kong alone.

In no time at all, I was back where I started. The taxi left me off curb side at the bar. I paid him the more than reasonable one Hong Kong dollar fare and he was off in a flash. Soft music poured out of the now unattended, but opened doorway to the bar. Where was my pertinacious friend? Maybe he took a piss call? Anyway, I was glad he wasn't there. It was the last thing I needed—a sarcastic remark on why I was back so soon.

I walked into the dimly lit bar and found it only a bit more lively than my hotel lounge. A juke box was playing American oldies, a few people occupied booths along the right wall, and several girls sat together giggling at a table near the door. Along the back wall at the small but adequate bar, a lone American sat nursing a scotch on the rocks. I pulled up a stool next to him and ordered a rum and coke. "Been here long?" I asked.

He slowly looked at me and answered with glazed, half-closed eyes, "Yup. Leaving tomorrow."

I tried to keep the conversation going, "Who are you with in Nam?"

"The 101st Airborne," he slurred.

I knew this was going to be a tough conversation. "I just arrived a few—" suddenly I was interrupted by a tap on my left shoulder.

"Hey, GI. Where you hotel? When did you get here? How much money you have?" All of these questions were fired at me by a well-dressed middle-aged mama-san.

"I just got here," I told her and went back to my previous conversation.

The next thing I knew, I felt an arm slip around my waist and a much higher-pitched voice sensually greeted me as I turned around. "Hi! My name is Teresa." I was seduced in that very second. In front of me stood a sensuous oriental girl with sparkling dark brown eyes, long straight jet-black hair, and a voluptuously demure smile. She was wearing high heels and was poured into a sleek red satin dress that was slit on the sides all the way up to her waist. She took my hand tenderly in hers and softly asked in heavily Chinese-accented English, "Would you like to come sit with me in a booth?"

I sprang at the opportunity. "Sure!" I exclaimed, grabbing my drink in one hand and her waist in the other. We left the bar abruptly, leaving the GI as I found him—nursing his drink alone.

Seated opposite each other in a booth near the front door, we were soon engaged in idle conversation. Out of nowhere, a waitress appeared at our booth and placed a drink down in front of Teresa.

"Teresa's thirsty," announced the waitress.

"Okay, how much?" I asked.

"Ten Hong Kong dollar," she replied.

I nursed my drink as we became better acquainted. I was infatuated with her unadorned beauty and fascinated by her accent. Within minutes the waitress reappeared at our booth. Teresa had hardly touched her drink, so I ordered only a refill for myself. When the waitress promptly returned with my drink, she had one for Teresa as well. As she placed it down in front of her, I looked up at the waitress inquisitively and tersely said, "I know. . . . Teresa's thirsty!" She could only giggle as I paid for both drinks.

Then Teresa abruptly asked, "You want to buy me? You buy no more drinks. I tell Mama-san you buy me, okay?"

I was astonished by her sudden candid solicitation. Then, without any further thought, I readily agreed. "Okay! How much?" I inquired.

"I come right back. I talk to Mama-san," she answered.

Teresa left and returned moments later, slipped into the seat next to me, and snuggled close. She paused for a moment, gazing coyly into my eyes. As I looked back into hers they shimmered in the delicate candlelight from the table. "You buy me for five days?" she asked softly.

"How much for five days?" I asked again.

"Three hundred Hong Kong dollar," she shyly replied.

I quickly calculated the exchange rate in my head and was surprised at the answer I arrived at. I had to double check it to be sure I was correct. It worked out to be less than the cost of my hotel room for the same amount of time. "Sounds okay to me!" I told her excitedly.

"You pay Mama-san," she said, obviously pleased at my decision.

We left shortly after and strolled hand in hand to my hotel. As we made our way only a short distance, she abruptly announced to me, "I cherry girl."

I chuckled tactlessly. "Oh, is that so!"

"I am!" she politely insisted. I raised her hand to my lips and kissed it gently. Then I offered a warm smile as an apology. I thought it best to drop the subject at that point. We walked the remainder of the way in silence.

Once in my room, her shyness prevailed. I undressed and climbed into the bed nearest the window as she disappeared into the bathroom. Lighting a cigarette, I lay there wallowing in the delightful anticipation. A few moments later she appeared clad in a bath towel and coyly approached the bed. I held out my hand, silently inviting her to join me. "Please, don't look at me. I don't want you to see me undressed," she bashfully whispered.

A chivalrous smile erupted as I complaisantly rolled onto my side toward the window. I had to wait only seconds till I felt the magnificent softness and pleasing warmth of her naked body pressing tenderly next to mine. At the same instant, I caught a wisp of her provocative perfume. It heightened my burning desire to make love to her.

Reaching over, I caressed her silky perfumed hair. Then slowly I kissed my way down from her forehead until our lips met in fiery passion. She responded in like kind, embracing my body close to her's and with calculated deliberation delicately darted her tongue into the depths of my mouth. Deeply embroiled in passion, I continued kissing my way down to the nape of her neck, occasionally leaving behind small passion marks. At the same time, I cupped her petite breasts in my hands and felt her nipples harden with my touch. Flicking my tongue over her sensuous nipples brought her panting wildly. Gently rolling her on to her back, I carefully inserted my throbbing manhood deeply into her moistened pussy. The resulting sensation was indescribable. She moaned with pure pleasure and wrapped her legs around my waist squeezing tightly. With rhythmic cadence we soon burst into sheer ecstasy.

After a brief interlude, her amorous glances lead us once more to rapturous fulfillment. Soon afterward, we were asleep in each other's tender embrace.

Sleeping late that morning, we were suddenly awakened when the hotel maid entered through the door with her passkey to make up the room. Teresa let out a screech and bolted out of bed, pulling the bed sheet with her. She bounded onto the adjacent bed and stood there with her back to the wall out of sight of the maid. I was left lying on the bed stark naked and in full view of the maid. I found the situation quite amusing and had difficulty trying to tell the maid to return later through my laughter. Realizing her blunder, the maid swiftly retreated with embarrassed apologies. As the door slammed closed, Teresa relaxed from her position of concealment and I burst into convulsive laughter. With that she became indignant. "Please, don't laugh at me. I don't find it funny at all. As you have discovered, I'm very shy girl and still have dignity." Again, I found myself apologizing for my insensitive behavior.

With the morning already in the past, we decided to have lunch at the Presidential Hotel. We took a taxi there, for it was not within quick walking distance. The restaurant was lavish, lending credence to its namesake. The food and service were impeccable. (Regretfully, we never dined there for dinner.)

At lunch we conducted the usual chitchat. I was intrigued with her obviously non-Chinese name and inquired, "Teresa is not Chinese. . . . "

"Oh, no!" she abruptly exclaimed. In almost a whisper she continued, "Teresa is my American name. I chose it when I work for Mama-san. Mama-san say American GI like girl with American name. My real name is Mai Ling." Then she perked up and asked, "Which one do you like?"

"I like them both. One is as pretty as the other," I answered tactfully. She merely blushed at my reply. "I'm curious. Where do you live?"

"I share an apartment with a girl friend, not far from your hotel," she answered. "I'll take you there later."

After lunch, Teresa suggested that we walk back and take in the sights along the way. It was a beautiful day outside and not a cloud in the sky. We left the hotel and strolled among the people on the crowded streets, inhaling the smells of various foods being prepared, dodging rickshaws, stopping to window shop, and browsing through the wares of the street peddlers. On one narrow side street, I was approached by an enterprising young boy offering chopsticks for sale. The price was right—one Hong Kong dollar. Teresa interpreted the Chinese inscription they held. It read: Eternal health and happiness.

On the way to her apartment, we passed a bank, which gave me the idea of transferring some additional money from my account in the States to this bank. We stopped in and inquired about the procedure. I found that it was quite simple and made arrangements to have two hundred dollars drafted from my account. The helpful bank official informed me it would take thirty-six hours and to return when the bank opened in two days.

I told Teresa that I wanted to stop back at my hotel before we did anything else. She asked if I would mind going on alone and said she would meet me at her apartment in two hours. She didn't explain why, but I agreed. Before we parted company, she pointed out her building and said she would meet me out in front.

Once back at my hotel room, I took a quick shower. Afterward, I decided to take a leisurely walk around before meeting Teresa. On the way I passed a clothing store and was promptly coaxed into looking around inside. Talk about high-pressure salesmen! I had no intention of purchasing suits or anything else in the way of clothes, but no matter how hard I tried to leave the store, the salesman was that much more determined to make a sale. There was hardly any room to move through the aisles; it was almost claustrophobic. He blocked my egress by pulling out bolt after bolt of material and insisting that I feel the texture of each, extolling the qualities they possessed and what wonderful suits they would make. Finally, I agreed to purchase two custom-made dress shirts just to satisfy him and get out of there. He guaranteed that they would be ready by the time I had to leave Hong Kong.

When I met Teresa, I related to her my captive experience while at the clothing store. She simply smiled and told me she would accompany me to the store when the shirts were ready. Then Teresa informed me that we were invited to a birthday dinner party for Mama-san that night. She said that all the girls who worked at the bar were invited with their escorts. It sounded interesting and I agreed to go along with her.

Once at her apartment, she apologized for its meager size. It was a single fairly good-sized room, utilized as a bedroom, living room, and dining area all in one. One wall held a large closet, while the opposite held a door to a rather small bathroom. It was well kept, clean, and quite femininely decorated. A large bed consumed a good portion of the room, and we soon found ourselves romping on it.

"Where is your roommate?" I asked. "Does she work at the bar, too?"

"No! She is a student. She does not want to work at the bar because she wants to marry a Chinese man. To do this a girl must be cherry or no Chinese man will marry her," she said sadly.

"I see," I mumbled, feeling as though I were responsible for her sudden sadness.

Then, a second later, she cheerfully exclaimed, "But do not worry. She will not be home for several hours!"

One thing lead to another and we were soon entwined in a passionate embrace. She fumbled to unbuckle my belt and, once open, struggled to unzip my trousers. At the same time, I nimbly unbuttoned the tiny buttons of her satin blouse. When she finally succeeded, I reached down to remove her panties. To my delightful surprise, I found only the silky-soft erotic skin of her sumptuous thighs awaiting my touch. Her softness heightened my fervor threefold. Wasting no time with turning down the bed sheets, we impetuously made love until we were both blissfully exhausted.

As we lay in each others arms on top of the crumpled bedspread, I gently stroked her silky hair and basked with contentment. Wondering to myself why she chose not to return to my hotel room with me, I asked, "Teresa . . . why didn't you come along with me after our walk? Was there something wrong?"

She lifted her head and softly kissed my cheek, after which she paused for a moment and then coquettishly answered, "Most bar girls stay with GI at night then go back and work at bar in daytime. But I want to stay with you. I went to see Mama-san and tell her so. Is that okay?"

I was flattered. "Of course it's okay; it's more than okay," I whispered kissing her forehead.

Later that evening, we took a taxi from my hotel to the party. It was a rented banquet hall on the second floor of a building that housed several small shops on the lower level. Upon our arrival, Teresa informed me that it was to be a catered affair and that many of Mama-san's friends and business acquaintances were invited. I had no idea what to expect from a Chinese birthday party, but thought that it would probably be somewhat formal and follow whatever traditional Chinese customs govern that type of affair.

Well, I was right to a degree and made myself look foolish immediately upon entering the reception room. I simply followed Teresa's lead and selected a slightly warm and neatly folded finger towel from a tray offered by an impeccably bedecked waiter at the door. Teresa hesitated briefly inside the doorway, which was just long enough for me to wipe my hands. The waiter remained facing me, as I suppose was proper etiquette, standing stiffly erect with tray in white-gloved hands. Feeling a bit awkward and misconstruing his courteous action, I committed a blunder by placing my used towel back onto the tray. He immediately let loose with a demeaning barrage in Chinese. From the look on his face it must have been a contemptuous admonishment, to say the least. Teresa swiftly turned and took hold of my arm, saying, "No! No!"; then she directed a seething retort at the waiter. I simply smiled and quickly retrieved my towel. I felt silly having my honor defended.

As we walked further into the room, I said softly to Teresa. "I'm sorry. I take it I wasn't supposed to do that. Just what was it that he said, anyway?"

"He was telling you that it wasn't correct to put a dirty towel back," she replied. Then she abruptly changed the subject. "Come, I introduce you to Mama-san," she said, tugging on my arm. Somehow I got the feeling there was something she left out.

In no time, the room filled with people and we were soon ushered to our assigned tables for dinner. There were several very large tables where the guests sat in order of age, or so it seemed to me. At the head table sat Mama-san and the eldest of guests. The next table seated younger guests and so on around the room. Seated at our's were the other girls from the bar and their escorts—twelve in all.

A brief toast offered to Mama-san signaled the beginning of the meal. Soon many waiters appeared, serving each table with course after course of various local delicacies. I recognized some of the dishes as they were served, but wisely chose to taste each before inquiring of Teresa on just what it was I was eating. The meal consisted of various sea food, local vegetables, rice in various artistic forms, exotic meats, chicken, and other traditional foods. Most were tasty, some were rather bland, and others I had great difficulty getting down.

The waiter at our table, like those at each of the other tables, served the food in a flamboyant style. He would divvy up the portions from the main platter, which was placed in the center of the table, with skilled precision; then he swiftly and courteously served counterclockwise around the table.

When the soup arrived steaming hot, it possessed a wonderful aroma. It was ladled into small bowls and served with a traditional Chinese short-handled shallow porcelain spoon. I consumed it in earnest, commenting to Teresa on its savory flavor. Believing that it was chicken soup, I was shocked to learn that I had consumed turtle soup. Still and all, it was delectable!

One course led to another, and we soon arrived at the completion of the banquet. At the end of the dinner, an odd-appearing morsel of dessert was set next to each person's plate. It resembled a spongy chicken egg in both shape and size. Without hesitation, I tasted it. My impuslive action drew giggles from those watching around the table. I hadn't the slightest inkling as to why, but soon discovered that the spongy outside was merely a protective coating. It was the center that was intended to be eaten. I had no choice then but to shrink with embarrassment and join in the laughter at myself.

The party went on quite late that night; however, Teresa and I gracefully departed, as did most of the other younger guests, and . went on our separate ways.

The next day, we decided to do a little sightseeing. We took a leisurely stroll to the waterfront and boarded a crowded ferry headed for the island of Hong Kong. While on board, Teresa indicated her discomfort caused by the stares she received from some of the local people because she was in my company. I did my best to distract her attention, but no matter what I said, I knew it bothered her just the same.

Once docked, we hurried to catch the train that transported us to the top of a steep mountain. The angle off accent was quite severe and there were many stops along the way. During the trip up, one was pressed by gravity backward into the hard wooden seats. It was an odd experience. Raised wooden planks were provided on the floor of the center aisle to facilitate walking at the steep angle.

Having arrived at the last station, it was only a short trek on foot to a delightful restaurant located at the very top. A shaded terrace overlooked the far side of the mountain and provided a breathtaking view of the modern business district and the ship-filled bay sprawled far below.

We had lunch in the light breeze of the shaded terrace. As we ate, I pondered my good fortune. There I was having lunch with an enchanting oriental girl in a terribly romantic setting so far away from the dangers and ills of a war that I had been in the midst of less than forty-eight hours ago. What more could one ask for? I was in seventh heaven. Suddenly, with startling dismay, the thought had entered my mind that all of this would soon end with my return to Nam. I instantly dismissed that repulsive thought and focused my undivided attention on Teresa's alluring brown eyes.

After a few hours of wandering around, we backtracked, taking the train down the mountain, the ferry across to Kowloon, and a taxi back to my hotel.

Once we arrived there, neither one of us had much of an appetite, so we decided to hibernate in my room for the evening. Hibernate we did, inactive we weren't. By the time midnight rolled around, not only was I pleasantly exhausted, but also extremely hungry as well. Merely making mention of the fact that I was hungry motivated Teresa to cheerfully volunteer to dress and fetch me whatever it was that I desired to eat. I was astounded by her willingness to please me. Thanking her for the unselfish offer, I told her that it wasn't necessary and that we would both go out together.

Teresa took me to a small out of the way restaurant where the food was well prepared and inexpensive. Several hours later, we had sufficiently satisfied our hunger and were once again back in my room. Anticipating that we would be sleeping late, I remembered to place the do not disturb sign on the door so that there wouldn't be an unexpected intrusion.

Over brunch at the Presidential Hotel late the next morning, we planned the day's activities. The bank was first on my agenda to pick up my money. After that, I was wide open for suggestions.

Teresa informed me that we had an invitation to dinner at her girl friend's apartment that evening if I chose to accept. I was quite receptive, finding the invitation intriguing. Then, out of the clear blue sky, Teresa suggested that we go bowling. Again, I was surprised. I suppose I didn't expect to find a bowling alley in Hong Kong.

That afternoon, after my banking transaction, we went bowling. The alleys were quite modern and kept in good condition. Out of the twenty-five alleys that the place held, only a few were in use when we arrived. I was never much of a bowler and Teresa was obviously still a novice, throwing more gutter balls than anything else. Nonetheless, we enjoyed ourselves and played several games. When we were finished, we changed shoes and headed for the desk with our score sheet to pay for the games. At the desk, I handed the clerk the sheet and our shoes. He had a shit-eating grin on his face and directed some kind of witty remark to Teresa in Chinese. Teresa knew even before I asked and translated for me what the clerk said: "You should have left the shoes at the alley, that way the employees who are paid by him to collect the shoes wouldn't become lazy."

I didn't find his attempt at humor very amusing and tried to keep my cool. Teresa must have realized that I wasn't amused and instinctively hurried me away from the counter and out through the door. "You should not act that way; he was only being friendly," she scolded.

That night, we arrived at her girl friend's apartment promptly at 1930 hours. It was in the same building as Teresa's, just down the hall a few doors. As we walked to the door, Teresa coyly informed me that, unlike herself, Kim worked independently, but, nonetheless, was a lady of the night.

We were greeted at the door by Kim and ceremoniously welcomed. I was totally enamored by her bewitching beauty. She was almost angelic looking, slightly taller than Teresa, and had typically long black hair drawn back loosely into a large pony tail and draped over her left shoulder. Her eyes were the color of ebony, and her high cheek bones accentuated her charming smile.

As we stepped through the doorway, I realized that she was dressed in nothing more than a rather provocative pink negligee. And one could easily see that beneath it she wore only a pair of powder blue panties. She had to know that she would unmercifully captivate my attention.

Standing in the corner of the room and unnoticed by me until I was introduced was Kim's mother. Another unexpected surprise. I soon learned that mother and daughter shared the apartment and that it was her mother who was preparing dinner for us that night. After a brief introduction, her mother returned to the task of preparing the meal. Teresa and Kim immediately became engaged in girlish conversation. Listening with a deft ear, I watched in disbelief through the open bathroom door as the old Mama-san prepared our supper stooped over a hot plate on the tile floor! Right then, I began to seriously doubt the wisdom of my accepting the dinner invitation, despite Kim's seductive titillation.

In no time at all, it was announced that the food was ready. We all pitched in, rearranging the furniture. A folding card table and three folding chairs were placed in front of a hideaway bed. Then the table was set with beautifully decorated dinnerware and wooden chopsticks. The three of us were instructed to be seated. Mama-san served each of us before she took her place at the table to my right. Teresa sat to my left and Kim sat across from me on the hideaway bed. She was most distracting sitting there, for she made no attempt to change her attire before dinner. I had all to do but to keep from drooling on my plate.

Whatever distasteful thought I had for food prepared on the bathroom floor, it soon vanished as we ate. On the whole, my one and only home cooked Chinese meal was quite an experience. To my surprise, I enjoyed almost everything. Wishing not to appear discourteous, I finished every bit of each portion served on my plate, even those I found not to my liking. No sooner had I consumed the last mouthful than did Mama-san refill my plate over my ardent declination. In a near panic, I turned to Teresa, knowing that Mama-san spoke only Chinese, and implored, "Please tell Mama-san that I am pleasantly satisfied and that I don't want any more!"

"Oh! Mama-san thinks that you didn't have enough to eat. It is customary *not* to leave your plate empty when you're full," she replied with a whimsical giggle. Looking at Kim, I saw that she had joined in with Teresa's giggling, and Mama-san continued replenishing my plate.

"*Now* you tell me!" I said, annoyed at her. Having learned my lesson, I ate a small portion and left the rest on my plate.

With dinner over, Kim politely excused herself to make ready for an unexpected rendezvous with a client for later that night. We took that as our signal to leave. I expressed my delight with the dinner invitation and of meeting Kim and her mother. Especially Kim! We said our good-byes and departed.

For all intents and purposes, the fifth and last day of my R&R began much the same as all the others—with breakfast at the Presidential Hotel. Then it was off to the clothing store to pick up the shirts that I was bamboozled into buying. Teresa intervened when the store clerk attempted to overcharge me by a considerable amount. With an outburst that I didn't realize she was capable of, she made it clear that she would not tolerate their unscrupulous behavior. The ferocity of her rage was reminiscent of a mother's instinct to protect her offspring from an unseemly transgression. As it turned out, I got the shirts at less than cost, thanks to Teresa's tour de force.

When we left, we walked around the corner to Teresa's apartment and spent the remainder of the afternoon engaged in rapturous bliss. Teresa received a call while we were at her apartment. It was a girl friend wishing to get together that night for dinner and a show. I agreed, thinking that it was appropriate for my last night in Hong Kong. Teresa collected a change of clothes and brought along various odds and ends to my hotel room.

That night, we met her friend and her American GI escort at a prearranged location. Together, we took a cab to the hotel supper club. The restaurant was very elegant, the service excellent, and the food most enjoyable.

As the floor show began, we had completed our dinner and were sipping on cocktails. At first, it was very entertaining. Several dancing girls scantily dressed in sequined outfits danced and sang a few numbers and there was even a comedy act, all of which actually were done quite well. Then the bombshell: Teresa and her girl friend knew all along that the performers had been women impersonators. At first, I thought they were joking, but soon realized that they were not. It didn't seem to bother them, but to me and the other American the very thought was repulsive. In disdain, we left without finishing our cocktails.

Once outside, I admonished Teresa for not telling me ahead of time about the show. She apologized for incorrectly anticipating my reaction. At that point, we parted company with Teresa's friend and her escort and headed back to my hotel.

When we arrived, I gambled that Harvey may have checked into the same hotel upon his arrival in Hong Kong. I knew he was due to arrive sometime that day. I called the front desk and inquired as to whether or not he registered. To my surprise and delight I learned that he was. His room was on the floor above mine. I quickly dialed his room number and he answered. When I heard his voice I asked, "Hey, Harvey, how the hell are you?"

"Who's this?" he asked with obvious puzzlement.

"It's me . . . Ski!" I told him.

"No shit! Where are you?" he asked excitedly.

"In my hotel room," I answered.

"Well listen, I'm at the Grand Hotel—"

I interrupted, "I know, Harvey! I called you, remember? My room is right downstairs from yours in the same hotel." By then I could tell that he was already a few sheets to the wind.

"Why don't you come up for a drink? I've got a bottle of rum!"

"Okay, but we're not staying long. Tonight's my last night and I'm going to make the most of it," I told him.

"I'm in room—"

Again I interrupted, "I know, Harvey, I know. I'll see you in a few minutes. Good-bye."

When we knocked on his door, he answered wearing only a pair of trousers and with a bottle in hand. I was glad to see him. I told him that I was astonished that we ended up in the same hotel together. In the room with him was a co-worker of Teresa's. They sat and talked as Harvey and I shot the shit over a few swigs from his bottle. Only a half an hour had passed when I decided it was time to go. As we reached the door on the way out, Harvey made a comment, something to the effect that he was now sure about my virility due to the fact that I was with Teresa. He said that he had some doubts ever since we were in the skivvy house together around the Fourth of July.

"Fuck you, Harvey!" I said as we departed. "I'll see you back on the hill in a few days."

Once back in my room, Teresa and I made passionate love to one another without once mentioning that our ways would part forever the next morning. I fell asleep holding Teresa closely in my arms.

A sudden knock came at the door. It was the early morning wake up call I had requested the night before. Teresa was startled by the sound and began to weep. I gently kissed away her tears, telling her that I would always cherish the time we spent together. She responded in kind as she regained her composure.

By 0800 hours, my things were gathered together and we went to the main lobby. She waited with me there for the shuttle bus that was to take me to the airport. We were not alone; others were already waiting as well. When the bus arrived, we embraced for the last time. Her eyes swelled with tears and she whispered, "I love you." I kissed her quivering lips and whispered good-bye. As the bus pulled away, I waved to her and sighed with deep regret that I had to leave.

In no time, the bus pulled up to the main building at the airport. As I departed the bus, I caught a glimpse of who I thought was Teresa getting out of a taxi. There was a sea of people carrying luggage entering the doors of the airport building. Teresa was soon lost in the shuffle. I called to her several times, but the sound of my voice was masked by the overwhelming noise of the crowd. My heart was racing as I forced my way toward her through the mass of GI's. When I finally reached her, I called, "Teresa! What are you doing here?"

She turned and an elegant smile radiated across her face. "I just wanted to say good-bye one more time," she replied, resting her head to my chest.

I kissed her fragrant hair and told her, "I'm pleased that you did."

We made our way to the area designated for my return flight and sat together in the lounge. Teresa kept me company the entire time I waited to board the plane. I relished the envious glances we received from the others waiting alone for the flight back to Nam.

The time had come for me to board the plane. Having already said our good-byes, I kissed her one last time. As I walked down the corridor I glanced back only to catch a fleeting glimpse of her tear-ridden face. The feeling I had at that moment was one of excruciating sorrow.

13.   Short-Timer

I had slept almost the entire flight and was awakened only by the sudden jolt as the plane touched down on the runway. When it finally came to a stop, the indelibly familiar mustiness and overwhelming heat poured through the forward hatch of the plane as it was flung open. No one made a mad rush for the door; each of us in our own good time made our way off the plane and out onto the tarmac. I felt refreshed on one hand and as though I weren't even gone on the other. How easy it was to revert back into the swing of things, I thought.

I caught the first transportation I could find back to the hill. Once I arrived in our area, the first thing I spotted was our freshly rebuilt ammo bunker. It appeared as though my squad did a real good job without me.

As I entered our hooch, I was eagerly greeted by those present. "Hey, Ski! How was R&R?" asked Oliver, slapping my back.

"Outstanding!" I exclaimed, grinning from ear to ear.

Ken and Al walked in right behind me. "Look who's back!" Ken shrieked.

"Did ya catch the clap?" joked Al.

"Fuck no! It ain't dripping," I retorted, grabbing my crotch.

I was relentlessly questioned by the guys about the five days I was on R&R. They wanted to know all the intimate details.

Then it was their turn. I was told of a terrible bout of crabs that had infected many of the men in our hooch while I was away. Almost no one went unscathed. The corpsmen dispensed a remedy to those affected. And as a precautionary measure the hooch had to be fumigated. A white powdery residue still clung around the inside of the hooch as the only remaining visual testimony. I seemed unable to sympathize and could do no more than chuckle at their misfortune.

A short time later, while waiting in line at the chow hall, several guys I casually knew made mention of the fact that I must have recently returned from R&R. The curious look on my face was enough for them to snicker and reply, "The hickeys on your neck are a dead giveaway, man. From the looks of it you must've had a good time!"

I returned a sly smirk and replied, "It was out-fucking-standing!"

I was glad that I was back on the hill in time for my dental appointment at 1530 hours that day. It had been cancelled once already and I wouldn't have wanted to reschedule it again.

The dental tent was located adjacent to the 105-mm battery just to the rear of our eighty-ones area. I was there promptly on time and was seen immediately by the dentist. No sooner had I sat in the chair when the nearby artillery battery began firing. From the sound of it, they must have been firing at a very low elevation and directly over the tent. The abrupt earsplitting report of the guns firing simultaneously scared the hell out of me, and I jumped out of the chair. "Holy shit! How the hell do you put up with that shit all the time?"

"You've got to have steady nerves," laughed the dentist.

Within days of my return, a platoon from Mike Company departed the hill on a routine daytime patrol. To their surprise, they walked in on a squad of hard-core NVA setting up a mortar near the foot of the battalion hill. A fierce fire fight ensued. The end results were the capture of one NVA squad leader and the annihilation of the men under his command.

Mike Company's spoils were freshly issued orders, maps, and various weapons, including two 82-mm mortars, a 60-mm mortar, a light machine gun, over sixty HE mortar rounds, hundreds of machine gun rounds, a few RPGs, grenades, and other miscellaneous small arms and equipment.

It was one of those times that luck, or fate, if you will, played a major role. Second Platoon had saved our hill from what would have been considerable destruction and loss of life. It was determined from the interrogation of the NVA squad leader and from the papers found in his possession that they were in South Vietnam for the first time. Their sole mission was to assault our hill. Their orders clearly instructed them to set up and fire five rounds in each of ten predetermined positions around our hill. Their map depicted with deadly accuracy the exact locations of the artillery batteries, 81-mm mortars, ammo dump, motor pool, the Battalion CO's hooch, chow hall, EM club, officers club, et cetera. They could have easily reeked havoc before we even knew what had hit us.

There was, of course, great dismay as to the source of their detailed map of our hill. It made one realize just how vulnerable we really were and how easily the enemy could extract intelligence from the general populace. Any so-called friendly gook allowed on our hill could pass along strategic bits of information and, more than likely, they very often did.

For the next few days, all of the hardware and ammo was layed out in a decorative fashion near the CO's hooch where it could be seen by all. Mortar rounds were stacked in neat little piles, belts of machine gun ammo were stretched out alongside the machine gun, grenades formed the letters *VC* in the center of the captured arms, and a helmet covered the muzzle of one of the 82-mm mortars.

Eventually, the Company CO turned over one of the 82-mm mortars and the 60-mm mortar to our mortar platoon, so that they could be cleaned up and displayed at the entrance to our area. A small wooden platform was constructed and the ordnance painted battleship gray. Then they were placed on permanent display.

A previously unannounced USO show was presented at the chow hall a few days later. The main event on the marquee was a Korean band featuring two female singers. Almost everyone on the hill was able to attend and were most grateful for the opportunity. The tables in the chow hall were moved to the sides to make room for everyone. Those in first were lucky enough to get a seat near the front. The rest stood in the back. Unfortunately, I was one of those in the back. The view from there was less than desirable, especially when one of the females in the group began her striptease act. It ended when she reached her skimpy two-piece costume, even though leering cheers from the audience urged her to continue. She wildly gyrated and undulated to the music as she danced. Her risqué performance was extremely erotic no matter what one's vantage point was! The band played a diverse repertoire of current songs and some oldies; hence, the show was a tremendous hit and a most pleasurable diversion for all.

It was the third day of March and I had become a short-timer with just thirty days left to go in Nam. It seemed most ironical that at that point I began to take more precautions than ever before. One became paranoid to a certain extreme, feeling as though the enemy was out to get you specifically. It was the strangest feeling! I remembered others expressing the same exact paranoia and I thinking they were a little *dinky dow*. Now I knew differently.

That night, not only was the moon absent from the sky, creating a situation where one could hardly see the hand in front of his face, but also it was when Sergeant Semcer threw the rule book out the window. He had concocted a plan, whereby all the guns were instructed to fire predetermined amounts of illumination. Each time setting had been precalculated and all the rounds plotted by him in advance.

We began firing what we all thought was a fire mission. We soon realized otherwise! As we fired on his cue, the illumination rounds popped one by one, revealing a salutation across the pitch-black sky. Whatever possessed him to conceived that irresponsible and idiotic stunt was beyond me. It read, Good-bye Al. My reaction was one of total disbelief. This man of ardent and steadfast compliance with rules and regulations had finally succumbed to incredible stupidity. We later learned it was a farewell to an obviously close friend of his who was rotating the following day.

The next morning, an inquiry was initiated by the Battalion CO to determine the person responsible for the inapprehensible act that had occurred the night before. I had no sympathy for him whatsoever, and in fact gloated over the jam into which he got himself. As far as I was concerned, they could have hung him by his balls; however, all he received was an Article 15 (a nonjudicial punishment under the Uniform Code of Military Justice).

The following day, just after noon, I was at the gook shop with Al and two of the new guys from my squad. Having picked up my laundry, the four of us were on our way back to the hooch when we heard the all too familiar chugginglike shwooshing sound of an incoming round passing over our heads. Immediately, the cry of "Incoming" resounded around the hill.

"What the fuck?" cried Al in disbelief.

"I don't know, but let's get the hell back!" I shouted.

We broke into an all-out run as we headed along the road to our area. I heard the first round hit, exploding to our right on the far side of the hill. It was followed in quick succession by a second round slowly cutting through the air overhead. It, too, landed long. By the time we reached our area, a third round swept overhead. I lunged for my gun pit and quickly donned my helmet and flak jacket. By then, all of our guns were manned.

Within seconds, we were given a fire mission. We fired two rounds each of HE in the direction of the incoming rounds. Not knowing the exact location, we bombarded a large area of the nearby mountainside. In addition to our firing, artillery let loose with a barrage of their own.

In spite of the intensity of our combined rounds crashing into the mountain side, the incoming rounds continued unaffected. The gooks ranged in on our hill by firing long and then walking the rounds back across the hill. The next two rounds landed in the artillery battery, exploding with terrific force.

When I looked, the new guys were huddled together on the ground of the gun pit as a subsequent round passed precariously overhead. "Get up! Get up!" I yelled. "It's the round you don't hear that you have to worry about!" But they didn't move. They were frozen with fear. I became so outraged that I grabbed hold of each one and yanked them to their feet, one by one. "What the fuck do you think you're doing? You're no fuckin' use to anyone down there!" I screamed at them over the profusion of noise.

I knew instinctively that if the rounds continued the next was destined for the center of our area. Each round had come at a precise interval and I cringed with anticipation of the next one landing on top of us. I held my breath, but the round never came. "They stopped!" someone shouted. God only knew why, but whatever the reason we were thankful.

"Holy shit! What the hell do they have up in that mountain, anyway?" asked Mike rhetorically.

"Probably a 75-mm recoilless rifle, firing at max range!" I suggested.

"Those son of a bitches are getting awfully daring, hitting us in the daytime like that!" added Mike.

"Yeah, no shit! First the NVA mortar squads and now this! They must be really pissed at us for something!" Nine-eight interjected.

"They just know I'm getting fuckin' short, that's all!" I said matter-of-factly.

Over the next few days, our hill was harassed by that 75-mm gun at various times of the day. We concluded that it was approximately three thousand meters northwest of our position. Both my gun and Harvey's were kept set up on the suspected area at all

times. If we got hit, we could immediately return fire and hope-
fully put it out of commission. The idea was sound, but in practice
it didn't work. Either the gun was too well dug in or it was moved
to a different position each day.

Early one morning, before chow, I was nearly shaken from
my rack. The ground jarred and rumbled with an awesome force.
In an instant, a sound resembling rolling thunder came from the direction of the mountainside.

"What the hell's going on?" someone yelled.

Those of us inside the hooch rushed out and peered in the direction of the mountain. What we saw was an early morning B-52
air strike called in along the mountainside. We cheered the high-altitude bombers: "Do a job on the motherfuckers!" Its payload of
five-hundred-pound bombs pulverized the entire area from thirty
thousand feet. We watched great plumes of earth and smoke
bellow into the air. Explosion after explosion sent shock waves
rippling through the mountain. The plane was invisible to the
naked eye, but the destruction it left in its wake was imposing.
From our vantage point, it seemed as though nothing could have
survived that kind of punishment.

Within minutes, the show was over and we as spectators went
about our business. As we walked back to the hooch Mike turned to
me and exclaimed, "I'm sure glad those B-52's are on our side! But
they could have at least warned us ahead of time."

"Yeah, they sure do some awesome damage. That was the
first time that I was ever so close to one of their air strikes," I reflected.

"I hear ya. Any closer and we would have been running for
cover ourselves!" There was a second of silence and then Mike continued, "I guess the VC got the point!"

"Yeah, I think they got the message all right, as Lou used to
say," I chucked and thought of Lou for a brief second.

At mail call that afternoon, I took a considerable teasing

about a perfumed letter addressed to me with a Hong Kong post-mark. I knew immediately that it was a letter from Teresa. I was pleasantly surprised that she had written to me. She had asked for my address, but I never expected to hear from her.

Her letter was intricately folded in a manner akin to origami. I remembered thinking that it fit her personality as I unfolded it. She wrote about the wonderful time we had together and how she thought of me ever since I had left. After reading her letter, I was left with a warm feeling inside.

That night, for the first time, I dreamt about being back on R&R and woke up feeling extremely melancholy.

The next day, we were hit again from the same mountainside. This time, it was only two rounds, just enough to let us know that they were still there. No one could believe that anything was left intact after the B-52 strike. The only thought was that they had a fortified concrete bunker out there.

Scuttlebutt soon began circulating about a large buildup of NVA in the mountains. Fear of another concerted offensive by the North was prominent in everyone's mind. It didn't take a strategy expert to realize that our hill sat precariously in a straight line between Da Nang and the NVA's reported position.

In the subsequent days, our battalion was officially put on the ready for a joint operation with several army units, which was to be conducted in those very mountains. Operation Oklahoma Hills had already begun on the first day of March, and we were soon to become actively involved in it.

As always, anxieties ran high. The entire hill was like a hornet's nest, with everyone gathering gear and swapping scutlebutt about our involvement in the operation.

I had less than two weeks to go, and I vehemently objected to going out on that operation. "I am too short for this shit," I kept telling myself.

One could imagine, then, how elated I was when I got the

word that anyone with less than twenty-one days left to his tour would remain in battalion. In all, that included Harvey, Oliver, and myself.

While the time passed slowly during those waning days, I didn't care. I knew I was going home. "Fuck this place!"

14. The World

Ten days later (28 March 1969) at 1000 hours, I received my orders, along with Harvey, from the battalion clerk's office. It directed the two of us to proceed that afternoon to the Marine Transient Facility in Da Nang.

It was home to the World! We were exuberant when we found out! We both literally jumped for joy. We shouted the good news to everyone within earshot, proclaiming, "We are skying out of here!" We had little time, though, to pack up our personal belongings, survey our combat gear, say our good-byes, and catch the admin run to Da Nang.

I raced around like a chicken with its head chopped off. Ken and Al gave me a hand packing my seabag with everything I wanted to take home. There were a few things I thought would be better used by some of the guys in the platoon. Al didn't have a rain jacket, so I gave him mine, and Nine-eight needed a pair of rain pants. I had no need for a rain suit where I was going; there was no monsoon season back in the World. Ken had an eye on my camera, so I sold it to him for ten dollars—a bargain if there ever was one.

Harvey had surveyed his weapon and gear while I was packing. When he returned, I noticed that my M-16 was missing. I had placed it right by the door of the hooch. "Hey, Harvey! You turned in my weapon, you dumb shit!" I complained.

"No I didn't! I turned in my own. Mine was right here by the door."

"Yeah? Well so was mine. And now it's gone!" I said in a panic. "Fuck it! I'm turning in whose ever this one is!"

I rushed down to supply and surveyed my gear. I had no problem; they didn't check the serial number on the M-16.

In the remaining time before the admin run was ready to roll, we said our emotional good-byes. When it came time, a few of the guys stood around wishing us luck back in the World. "Be careful out on that operation you guys," I called back as the six-by lurched forward. We waved until they were out of sight.

Harvey and I were the only two in the back of the six-by. We sat quietly without uttering a word. From time to time, we simply smiled at each other, knowing we were going home. A warm breeze swept through the open truck. The jarring ride conjured up memories of when we first arrived in country. Like the first time, we were again riding through Nam with no weapons. Only this time I didn't care.

With seabags on one shoulder and ditty bag in the other hand, Harvey and I marched into the transient facility. Our orders were checked and stamped. The officer checked his roster and scribbled in the flight date and the number. We were flying out the next day at 1215 hours on flight H27. We had one last night to go in Nam.

Next, our bags were inspected for any contraband. No weapons, grenades, C-4, flares, or marijuana could be taken aboard the plane. Even photo albums were checked for unseemly photos.

After finding an empty bunk in the building next door, Harvey and I headed for the PX to pass the time. I made a few small purchases and treated myself to my last haircut and massage in Nam. That night I slept like a baby.

The next day, precisely at noon, with anticipation at its greatest, we boarded the commercial airliner and buckled ourselves into our seats. When the plane was loaded and hatches secured, the AC was kicked on by the pilot and a cool surge of air circulated throughout. The engines whined as we taxied to the runway. The pilot's voice came over the PA cutting the silence. "Welcome aboard the Freedom Bird." There was a loud spontaneous cheer. The captain continued, "We should be out of here in just a few short minutes, as soon as we receive clearance from the tower. Please fasten your seat belts and extinguish all smoking materials."

After what seemed like forever, the plane gradually rolled down the runway and was finally airborne. I peered out of the window and watched pensively as the ground rushed farther and farther away. Once we sensed that we were safely in the air, wild cheers filled the plane in ecstatic rejoice. As the cheers subsided, a voice from the rear screamed out, "Fuck the Nam!" Everyone hailed the incantation.

Several hours later, the first leg of our trek home came to an end as we landed at Camp Butler, Okinawa. There we reported in at the transient facility at 1730 hours. All jungle utilities and jungle boots were taken away from us except one pair of each. I kept my new pair of jungle boots and surveyed the other. We were assigned sleeping quarters and told we would be informed later when our flight to the States was scheduled for departure. It was expected within a few days.

The next day, we attended a briefing and were issued the decorations that each of us was entitled to. Then we were split up according to our final destinations. Harvey's destination differed from mine. I was reassigned to El Toro, Marine Corps Air Station, Santa Ana, California, for separation from the Corps, and he was reassigned to Quantico, Virginia, via a twenty-day leave.

One night, on extremely short notice, we were ordered to get ready to fly out within two hours. We were told it was a full day ahead of schedule. I had no one to say good-bye to; Harvey had already flown out the day before.

Once on the plane, we endured a long and exhausting flight back to the continental USA. When we landed in El Toro, our plane taxied to a receiving area and we climbed out into the much cooler climate of early April in California. The temperature was in the low 80s.

We were met by an enthusiastic cub scout pack waving American flags and displaying a banner that read "Welcome Home." The experience left me feeling somewhat cheated and angry. Not at the cub scouts—I appreciated their effort—but at society in general. We had just returned from a war and no one seemed to care! I was actually shocked to find out that there was such protest toward the war and disdain for those of us that fought in it. Didn't they know what we endured there? Why didn't they care about us?

The next few days kept us busy with the usual rigmarole of physicals, reenlistment talks, preparing uniforms, and paperwork. What should have only taken five days took a few days longer because of Easter falling early that year.

On 10 April 1969, I was separated from the Marine Corps and headed home with $177.36 travel allowance. I was proud to be a marine and to have served my country, no matter what anyone else thought to the contrary. And I took solace in the inscription embroidered on the back of my camouflage poncho liner jacket, which read, "When I die I'll go to heaven, because I've served my time in hell!"

With the mounting dissension and increasing contempt directed toward the military by so many people etched vividly in my mind, I locked away the scarring and sobering experiences of the past thirteen months. From that time on, those experiences were only shared grudgingly in private conversations with other veterans of Nam, for they were the only ones who understood!

Glossary

ADMIN. Administrative.

ADMIN RUN. Regularly scheduled trips to another command to deliver or retrieve dispatches or personnel.

AK-47 (AK). Russian built 7.62-mm assault rifle used by the enemy.

AMMO BOARD. A rigid board carried on the back and used to transport ammo.

AMMO BUNKER. A sandbagged bunker used to store ammo.

AMMO HUMPER. A member of a mortar squad whose job it is to handle ammo.

AMTRACK. Marine Corps tracked transport vehicle.

APC. Armored personnel carrier.

AREA OF OPERATION. An area in which a military unit operates.

ARTY. Artillery.

B-52. High-altitude heavy bomber.

BABY-SAN. An unmarried oriental youth.

BODY BAG. A plastic bag used to transport dead bodies.

BODY COUNT. Confirmed kills.

BOO KOO. Vietnamese meaning "much" or "many."

BOOM-BOOM GIRL. A prostitute.

BOONIES. The field.

C-4. Plastic explosive.

CAP. Combined action platoon. A squad of marines and PF's in a compound on the perimeter of a ville.

CG. Commanding general.

CH-46. Marine Corps Sea King transport helicopter.

CH-53. Marine Corps Stallion heavy-lift cargo helicopter.

CHARGE. The amount of explosive needed to propel a round.

CHERRY. Newness; a new man.

CHIEU HOI. Open arms; a program of amnesty offered to VC or NVA defectors.

CHOPPER. A helicopter.

CIVVIES. Civilian clothes.

CLAYMORE MINE. An electrically detonated antipersonnel fragmentation mine.

CLICK. 1000 meters.

CO. Commanding officer.

COBRA. A swift, maneuverable gunship; AH-1G.

CONCERTINA WIRE. Coiled barbed wire.

CORDITE. Smokeless powder used in the production of ammo.

CORPSMAN. A navy enlisted man trained in the medical field.

CP. Command post.

C-RATS. Combat food rations sealed in cans.

DEFLECTION. The horizontal coordinate used to set up a mortar.

DETONATION CORD. Explosive cord contained in a waterproof covering.

DIDI. Vietnamese meaning "to go" or "leave."

DIDI MOW. Vietnamese meaning "go quickly."

DINKY DOW. Vietnamese meaning "crazy."

DOG TAG. US military identification usually worn around the neck.

DUNG LAI. Vietnamese meaning "stop."

E-FOUR. Marine Corps corporal; lowest NCO rank.

EIGHTY-ONES (81's). A mortar section consisting of two guns, an FDC, and an FO attached to a infantry company.

ELEVATION. The vertical coordinate used to set up a mortar.

EM. Enlisted man.

E-TOOL. Entrenching tool.

F-4 PHANTOM. A jet fighter–bomber used in tactical support of ground combat units equipped with bombs, rockets, and 20-mm Gatling gun.

FDC. Fire directional center.

FIRE BASE. An artillery position secured by infantry.

FIRE FIGHT. A gun battle.

FIRE MISSION. A call for fire by mortars or artillery.

FLAK JACKET. Body armor worn to protect from small arms fire and shrapnel.

FLICK. A movie.

FLIGHT DATE. Scheduled flight to return to the States.

FO. Forward observer.

FORTY-FIVE. Potent Oriental whiskey.

FOXHOLE. A hole dug into the ground for protection from enemy fire.

FRAGGED. An attempt to kill a fellow soldier.

FREEDOM BIRD. Slang for airplane back to the States.

FREE FIRE ZONE. An area designated to be under enemy control where anyone could be fired upon.

GOOK. The enemy; a derogatory term for an Oriental.

GOOK RUM. Vietnamese dark rum.

GOOK SHOP. A Vietnamese store located within a military compound.

GRUNT. An infantryman.

GUN PIT. A sandbagged circular area in which a mortar is operated.

GUNSHIP. An armed helicopter.

GUN WATCH. Duty on a mortar.

H&I. Harassing and interdiction.

H&S. Headquarters and Service.

HE. High explosive.

HEAT TAB. A small rectangular flammable tab used to heat C-rats.

HOLE WATCH. Duty in a perimeter bunker.

HONCHO. Someone in charge.

Hooch. Living quarters.

Hot LZ. A landing zone under enemy fire.

Huey. Fast and heavily armed utility helicopter; UH-1's.

I Corps. Military command area that includes the five northernmost provinces in South Vietnam.

Illumination (Illum). A round used to light up an area.

Incoming. A term used to describe taking hostile fire.

In country. Being in Vietnam.

Increment. An explosive charge on a mortar round.

ITR. Infantry Training Regiment.

KIA. Killed in action.

Kit Carson scout. A Vietnamese used as a scout for the U.S. military.

LAAW. A one-time, disposable 66-mm antitank shoulder weapon.

Lifer. A career military person.

Long Binh jail. A military stockade at Long Binh.

LP. Listening post.

LZ. Landing zone.

M-16. 5.56-mm automatic rifle.

M-26. Fragmentation grenade.

M-60. 7.62-mm light machine gun.

MACV. Military Assistance Command, Vietnam.

Mama-san. A married oriental female.

Medivac. Medical evacuation from the field by chopper.

Mess duty. Mess hall duty; (KP).

Mike-mikes. Military slang for millimeters.

Million dollar wound. A noncrippling wound serious enough to warrant return to the States.

Mini-gun. Electrically operated 7.62-mm Gatling gun.

MOS. Military occupational specialty.

Motor pool. An area to store and repair military vehicles.

MPC. Military payment certificate.

Mule. A small four-wheeled vehicle used for hauling.

Nam. Vietnam.

NAPALM. Incendiary substance dropped by aircraft.

NCO. Noncommissioned officer.

NET. Radio network.

NVA. North Vietnamese Army.

OD. Officer of the Day.

OFFICE HOURS. Hearing by CO relating to nonjudicial punishment.

PAPA-SAN. A married oriental male.

PARRIS ISLAND.Marine Corps recruit depot in South Carolina.

PF. Popular forces; village defense units.

PFC. Private first class.

PRC-25. A field radio carried by an RO.

PRC-88. A field phone utilized between gun pit and FDC.

PREP-FIRE. To bombard an area with artillery or mortars before troops move in.

PLOTTING BOARD. A grid board used to plot fire missions on.

PURPLE HEART. U.S. military decoration awarded when wounded in action.

PX. Post exchange.

QUARTERMASTER. A military person in charge of supplies.

R&R. Rest and relaxation; usually five to seven days leave from Vietnam.

RE-UP. To request another tour of duty.

RIFLE BELT. A webbed belt worn around the waist to secure gear upon, such as canteens, magazines, holsters, et cetera.

RIFLE COMPANY. An infantry company consisting of HQ and several platoons.

RO. Radio operator; radioman.

ROAD SWEEP. A small unit of infantry utilizing mine detectors to secure roads from booby traps.

ROTATE. Return to the States after a tour of duty.

ROUND-EYE. Non-oriental person.

ROVING COMPANY. An infantry company without a permanent base.

RPG. Rocket-propelled grenade used by the enemy.

RUBBER LADY. Inflatable rubber mattress.

S2. Intelligence section.

SCUTTLEBUTT. Rumor.

SEABEE. Navy construction engineers.

SHITTER. Latrine.

SHORT. Being a short-timer.

SHORT-TIMER. Someone who has very little time before rotating.

SHORT-TIMER'S CALENDAR. A calendar used to count the days before rotating.

SHOT CARD. A record of immunization shots received to date.

SILVER BAR. Rank insignia of a first lieutenant.

SILVER STAR. U.S. military decoration awarded for gallantry.

SIX-BY. A two and one half ton truck.

SKIVVY HOUSE. A brothel.

SLOP CHUTE. Marine Corps slang for a club or bar.

SMALL ARMS. Small caliber weapons including handguns, rifles, and machine guns.

SP. Shore patrol.

SQUADBAY. Room in a barracks where personnel live.

STARLIGHT SCOPE. An image intensifier used to identify targets at night.

SURVEY. To turn in unserviceable items.

TET. Lunar New Year; Vietnamese holiday.

THREE-SEVEN (3/7). Third Battalion, Seventh Marines, First Marine Division.

TO. Table of organization.

TOUR. The length of a duty assignment.

TRACER. A round chemically treated to glow so that it could be followed in flight.

TRIP WIRE. A wire strung across an area to set off an explosive when hit.

UH-34. Marine Corps utility helicopter.

UTILITIES. Marine Corps work uniform.

VC. Vietcong.

VILLE. A village.

WATER BUFFALO. A large buffalo with large horns used as a draft animal.

WATER BULL. A container that holds drinking water.

WOOD LINE. A row of trees.

WORLD OF HURT. Idiomatic expression for a spiritual, emotional, or physical condition.

WORLD, THE. The United States.

WP. White phosphorus.

XIN LOI. Vietnamese for "sorry about that."

60-mm. A mortar. See 81-mm.

75-mm. A recoilless rifle used by the enemy.

81-mm. A mortar; smooth bore, muzzle loading, high angle of fire weapon utilized by the infantry.

82-mm. An enemy mortar.

105-mm. Light weight ground artillery; howitzer.

155-mm. Self-propelled howitzer.

175-mm. Heavy artillery mounted on a self-propelled tracked vehicle.